The number of people that leave public safety because of addictions to drugs, alcohol, domestic violence issues, or even worse suicide because of the impacts from post-traumatic stress from the things they have seen and the events they have been involved in, is creating a devastating trend in keeping an experienced and happy workforce. Tania's book provides real world steps that she has applied and that have worked in my organization and other organizations to save people that would have left the business, continued with addictive behaviors, or been unable to function because of the terrible effects of PTSD.

This book is not written from someone showing up to the latest movement to talk about how bad traumatic stress is in public safety, but it is written by a true professional that is has been working for decades to keep public safety professionals on the street and functioning in the world that many others don't see, hear, and will never understand.

As a thirty-two-year veteran in public safety, and the Chief Executive responsible for the safety and welfare of the community in which I work, I depend on the employees of the department to respond and take care of each person in a professional, efficient, and positive manner. This only happens when you have employees that are safe and well both physically and mentally.

Tania and the steps in this book will be the start in helping you get a plan to keep yourself, your peers, and your employees well and educated in how to address bad events when they must respond.

We all understand that we cannot change the images, sounds, and odors at the events we are exposed to in the line of duty, but we can change the impacts of those things on our careers by working with true professional like Tania and singing the guidance that comes for her book.

Bill Gardner, CFE, EMT-P
Fire Chief/Emergency Management
Coordinator, City of Leander

FIRST RESPONDER RESILIENCE:

CARING FOR PUBLIC SERVANTS

BY

TANIA GLENN, PSYD,
LCSW, CCTP

Text Copyright © 2017 Tania Glenn

Published 2017 by
Progressive Rising Phoenix Press, LLC
www.progressiverisingphoenix.com

ISBN: 978-1-946329-51-6

Printed in the U.S.A.

Editor: Jody Amato

Illustrations:
Colored Bull's-eye
©2007 Jim Belk. Used by permission
https://en.wikipedia.org/wiki/File:Colored_Bullseye.png.
Diagram of Maslow's Hierarchy of Needs
© 2006 J. Finkelstein. Used by permission
https://commons.wikimedia.org/wiki/Commons:GNU_Free_Doc
umentation_License,_version_1.2.

Author Cover Photograph: ©2017 Jill Hays Photography.

Book cover design by Kalpart.
Visit www.kalpart.com

Book interior design by William Speir
Visit: http://www.williamspeir.com

To Mike, my parents, and first responders everywhere—especially Denise, Miranda, and Jeremy, who all stepped up.

We are family.

Table of Contents

Foreword

Public safety professionals are on the front line, protecting citizens and property every day. Our police, fire, and EMS personnel represent the thin line between violence, pain, and destruction. But who takes care of our first responders?

First Responder Resilience: Caring for Public Servants was written to address this very issue. Tania Glenn has spent her entire career dedicating her time, efforts, and energy to assisting first responders. From preparing our public safety personnel on how to cope with trauma, to educating them on the impact of horrific events in preventative efforts to inoculate them to high-stress situations, to walking them through their healing processes, Tania has been with our heroes every step of the way.

First Responder Resilience: Caring for Public Servants is the guide to doing this very important work the right way. All too often, our public safety professionals are not provided with the care they need, or even worse, are subjected to forms of care that are inappropriate or harmful. The goal in caring for first responders is to get it right, every time.

As a member of the 160th Special Operations Group, I was assigned to D company, where I performed duties as Flight Lead and Standardization Instructor Pilot. I participated in combat operations Prime Chance, Just Cause (Panama invasion, December 1989), Desert Storm (Liberation of Kuwait, January to March 1991), and Restore Hope (Somalia, August to October 1993).

On October 3, 1993, while piloting an MH60 Blackhawk in Mogadishu, Somalia, I was shot down and held captive by hostile forces. I was released eleven days later.

I met Tania Glenn when we were both presenting at a conference in 2014. I told my story and educated the audience on lessons learned in preparation and resilience. Tania followed by educating first responders on the types of stress, normal reactions to stress, and combating post-traumatic stress disorder. While from very different worlds, our messages clearly meshed. Tania asked me to write the foreword for this book, and I am excited to participate in this important endeavor.

Michael J. Durant
US Army, CWO 4 (Ret.)

Introduction

In my twenty-sixth year of an amazing career as a clinician focused on mental resilience, I take care of employees in the fields of public safety, the military, and aviation. Healing employees who are caught up in and burned out by high stress and trauma, my job is to evaluate, assess, and treat people after they've experienced traumatic situations. Post-traumatic stress disorder (PTSD) is my main field of occupation. The work is difficult and hard-core. It requires absolute concentration, total mental immersion, and a fierce desire to pull a frayed, exhausted mind back to normal functioning. It's a draining job, but I love what I do, and I hope to do it for another twenty-six years.

According to my colleagues, former patients, and my family, this book is long overdue. I hope readers will find value in what I have to say. The only approach in my work—with a very diverse and specialized, high-energy, hard-charging, dedicated community—is to get it right. Not just part of the time, but 100% of the time. And when I say, "get it right," I mean: *hit the bull's-eye*. Merely hitting the target is not enough. Police officers, firefighters, paramedics, veterans, and flight attendants are generally hard-core, skeptical thinkers and when they need help, they need it *now*. And they need it to be right on. Effective intervention after trauma and getting professionals back in line is what I do.

My goal for this book is twofold: to help first responders understand what to do when dealing with trauma and to assist with effective intervention. I hope this book will guide clinicians to better understand what they need to bring to the table in order to care for this highly valued population. I hope this book will help managers and leaders realize the severity of traumatic situations, and learn how to ask for competent help for their personnel. And I hope peer support team leaders will gain an understanding of what to expect from a good clinician, and even guide professionals who may be in the dark to understand what is involved in today's traumatic responses. Most of all, I want my book will bring hope to the many who suffer.

Chapter 1
Have a Plan

So maybe I'm the one that needed saving
Someone to rescue me from myself
And now the memories are slowly fading
Wish I could see me through the eyes of someone else

"Rescue Me" by Digital Summer

The time to develop a plan is not when you need one. You *must* have a plan. And it must be in place *before* you need it.

This book is designed to serve as a resource guide for public safety professionals: police, fire, and EMS—all first responders. This is the population I have served for twenty-six years, along with active-duty military and veterans. This population is expected to manage situations the general public runs from. Whether violence, death, illness, accidents, abuse, or fire, first responders are trained to enter the realm of danger and despair, take control, stop the chaos, and render aid. A long-standing tradition holds these amazing men and women to just somehow "walk it off," "suck it up," or simply "get over it" when experiencing trauma from on-the-job situations. That doesn't work. It never has. Professionals, no matter how well trained, have a threshold for stress and trauma, just like the rest of us. When pushed beyond this threshold, people get overwhelmed. No one is immune to stress and post-traumatic stress disorder. No one.

From this point forward, I want readers to understand that we are officially taking "suck it up" off the table. It is not a coping mechanism, and it never has been. If you are an "old-school" leader who thinks "suck it up" is an effective thing to say, or the right attitude to have, I ask you to read this book in its entirety, especially the chapter on PTSD. I ask all leaders to understand that everyone is different in how they interpret trauma, and how they are impacted by certain events. Public safety professionals are trained to pull through events and stay strong until the crisis is over. This book is about how to keep your team resilient and on the line when the crisis ends.

One of the first programs I developed was for an EMS organization in the Central Texas area. I was twenty-four years old and beginning to build a specialized practice. I was fresh out of my master's program and already had a significant amount of experience with paramedics and EMTs through working at a Level II trauma center and joining them for ride-alongs. I called it the "Wellness Program" and essentially created the first program of its kind to keep first responders healthy. I presented my program to the Command Staff at this EMS organization by outlining possible services, costs, and performance measurements. At the end of the presentation, one of the commanders raised his hand and said, "So, essentially what you are telling us, Tania, is you are about to hand us a generation of pussies."

I was floored. I was angry. I explained to the commander that what I had outlined was designed to keep his medics on the line healthier, happier, and stronger in their jobs. The snide look I received in return summed up how he felt about the program. The director of the EMS organization thanked me for my presentation and explained there was really nowhere in the budget for such a program. On my way out the door, I turned to the group and said, "I know some of you don't believe in the program and perhaps some of you do. I believe so much in this program that I am going to do it for free and turn in my statistics every month until you see the value in it."

I ran the "Wellness Program," which was really more of a resilience program, for free for three years.

The statistics were astounding. Paramedics, EMTs, communications specialists, and even some administrative professionals came for help. Countless hours of therapy and critical incident callouts occurred. The calls for critical incidents usually sounded like this: "I don't know what to do for my crew, but they're not OK. Please help. Can you come to the station? Right now?"

Finally, one day the organization's director called and explained he had moved some money around and they were ready to put me on contract. I am forever grateful to this individual for what he did. The EMS Wellness Program was the first of its kind and remains the model for every program I run for all my customers. This model has served as the standard on how to help the helpers. Today this EMS organization is thriving in a rapidly growing city. Its personnel are some of the best in the country. Its culture is clear—we take care of our own, we ask for help, we stay healthy, and we look out for each other and for the rest of our community.

By the way, the commander who made the statement about the "generation of pussies" turned out to be the commander who called me the most for his crews following critical incidents. We formed quite a bond through all of it. He referred to me as the

Kumbaya Queen until he retired, so I referred to him as the Kumbaya Commander. It seemed to fit.

What's the Plan?

"I received your name from multiple people. I checked out your website. I know you don't know me, but please, can you come help us? I realize we don't have a contract with you, but we can make that happen." This is the typical call I get from organizations that have no plan in place to manage a crisis. It's frustrating. But even more so, it's heartbreaking.

The time for a plan is not when you need it. The time for a plan is now, in place before you need it. I've been contacted during or immediately after a crisis by countless agencies that have no plan in place, which delays services, and that delay results in personnel crumbling under the stress. Some of the agencies were able to get me out to help them because they had the internal structure to create a contract very quickly; unfortunately, others were unable to do so. Even when an agency is able to create a contract quickly, I consistently notice that I'm still starting at a deficit because either no services have been initiated, or the initial services were ineffective or poorly delivered. Trust me when I say that a group of first responders who don't know me and whose prior services were poorly delivered are not happy to see me at all. I have to climb my way out of a hole, with no credibility. I've seen the daggers in their eyes as they try to decide how quickly they can dismiss me. But, once I get started, things improve. Until that point, though, if looks could kill, I would not be writing this book.

Your plan should be kept simple and fit the needs of your particular organization. The main reason for having a crisis plan is to have all outside resources set up and ready. Since this book deals with the mental health and resiliency of first responders, I will focus on that. From the very beginning, it's important to have a complete list of all state, local, national, and federal resources available that can assist an agency through a crisis or line-of-duty deaths. A call to just a few of these resources often results in an amazing series of unexpected responses and unbelievable assistance.

Assistance for the mental health of first responders is typically the most overlooked factor because no one knows how to set up or manage this aspect of the plan. The first and best thing to do is to find a local clinician or clinical practice that seems to be a good fit for public safety personnel. I have outlined some concepts for clinicians who want to work with this kind of population later in the book. Department or contracted clinicians should always be trained to treat trauma. They should be well-versed in public safety terminology and lifestyles. They should understand the unique dynamics at play in public safety teams and families. Clinicians who work in public safety must go on ride-alongs. They must seek advanced training in trauma treatment. They must "get it."

Finding the right clinician is not easy. It's really about the right personality and attitude, in my opinion. If you can find a counselor who is excited and eager to learn, who enjoys riding along and participating in some of your calls, you have a winner. From there, you can train your clinician to understand the culture of public safety and your organization in particular. As this clinician's experiences and knowledge increase, you will notice they begin to also "speak the language." Whether it's a ten-code or a mention of a difficult intubation, the subtleties of the clinician's understanding of what first responders mean will resonate well with your personnel. Just as any new hire has to be trained for the job, the same is true for clinicians. They must be trained on how your crews work, and how they can help them when the time comes.

In my profession, the biggest mistake is to assume that just because clinicians are providers through your Employee Assistance Program (EAP), they are trained to understand what first responders do. I cannot count the times leaders, first responders, and family members have told me the same horror stories about the EAP counselor whose jaw dropped during a session; the EAP counselor who started to cry upon hearing the reason someone was seeking help; or the EAP clinician assigned to see police officers after a justified fatal shooting to clear the officers back for full duty, who then proceeded to tell the officers they should not feel good about the shooting because they killed someone. If one thing in my career makes me angry, it is this. Not only does it represent failure of epic proportion toward the client, it causes even more harm. Public safety professionals who have gone through terrible mental health experiences state they will never see a counselor again. I can't blame them for coming to this conclusion—I wouldn't either! I can honestly say that no mental health treatment is better than bad mental health treatment.

If the counselor you find locally is not on your EAP and doesn't want to participate in the EAP program, it's imperative that your department contracts with the clinician separately. Understandably, the leadership at whatever level you report to will question this and, as a leader in your department, you will need to justify why this clinician should be contracted outside of the EAP. My customers frequently use sole-source justifications to bring me on. The scope of the contract must be focused on the areas where services provided by your EAP program are inadequate: work-related trauma, post-traumatic stress disorder, and burnout. None of my contracts cover personal issues, such as child rearing or financial planning. That's what the EAP is for.

Once you have the right counselor on contract, the next steps are to incorporate the clinician into as much training as possible. Have the clinician provide training on trauma, resilience, and PTSD recognition and treatment. Invite the counselor to departmental training that might be relevant, such as disaster response, hostage situations, dealing with the mentally ill, and so forth. It will increase understanding, trust, and synergy on both sides.

As things progress, be sure to include the clinician in your disaster or critical incident plan. Set up a way to reach the clinician quickly and get to know his or her trusted back-up clinicians in case something happens and your primary clinician is out of town.

Be sure your clinician believes in and sets up peer support teams, which are imperative to any large-scale response. Without peer support, my job would be impossible. I train and utilize peer support as often as I can. When a department's peer support team is on the receiving end of services, I coordinate my other teams to come in and assist. The peer support process, when well run, is one of the best resources a leader can invest in.

A final note about contracting with a clinician: please remember, you're investing in picking the right person for your people, and you are asking your people to trust this person. You are choosing the best of the best to help you, and you want your personnel to get well and be well. One of the features of all my contracts is that there are never any names associated with the billing. Some of my customers simply want a total number of hours spent per month. Others ask for a random client ID to be assigned to each person so their department can track how long first responders spend in therapy, on average, for budgeting planning. They have no knowledge of who is assigned to which ID. All this is designed to protect the privacy and dignity of my patients. My very first contract—the EMS organization I mentioned earlier—was the first organization to set up the contract this way. The reason is simple: Public safety personnel will not come to therapy if there is a paper trail. Fear of being diagnosed or labeled—and the subsequent fear of losing jobs, badges, and guns—keeps them from seeing a desperately needed therapist. The only way to encourage them to come and reassure them their privacy is safe is to set up the contract and program in this manner. The bottom line is, you have to trust your counselor to bill ethically. No amount of money is worth the consequences of unethical behavior. And when you trust the right person to take on this role, you will serve your people to the best of your ability.

I want to finish this chapter with a comparison of two very similar air medical accidents. Both involved very significant crashes, subsequent horrific fires, burning of each aircraft, and death and injuries to personnel.

The first organization to have such a crash was not yet a client of mine. I met some of the leadership at an air medical conference and the company had requested a proposal, which I delivered. Upon hearing of the crash, I called one of the directors and offered my services. He returned my call, immediately requested help, and reported the company would generate a contract. He was very sincere and unnecessarily offered to give me his personal credit card as a sign of good faith. I responded immediately and worked with several personnel over the course of the next five weeks. In particular, I worked with the crew members who had been the first on the scene. We hit the ground running, and the crew members had a smooth transition back to work, without issues and certainly without PTSD (more on interventions later). I began working with them on the day after the crash, when the most impacted crew members exhibited thousand-yard stares, were crying, and were talking about quitting their jobs, to day twenty-seven, when all three members were back in the air on flight status. We worked hard as a team and each day these three amazing people got better and stronger. It was a twenty-seven-day transformation, involving five short trips to work with these incredible professionals, who represented one of the best experiences of my career. The lessons from this experience were many, but there were two main ones. First, my work would have been much easier had there been a peer support team; the following year I set up and trained that peer support team. Second, the total cost to bring me to the city where the incident had occurred was under $10,000, including travel costs. The cost to replace and train three crew members would have been $120,000. This does not reflect the costs typically incurred by an organization due to a crew member who may quit because of trauma, such as the use of sick leave and the Family and Medical Leave Act. Good care was a drop in the bucket compared to the cost of no care.

My second example, the second crash, was also with an organization that was not yet a customer. This program first tried using local resources, which didn't go well, and the attempts at helping those who were impacted completely failed, making their situations worse. Not only were the interventions not helpful, they severely angered those first responders to the crash. They were completely shut down to further help. I was contacted by the company about two weeks after the crash, when things were really unraveling, and made four trips to the city where this had occurred. There was so much resistance toward me on my first trip that my work was extremely difficult. I provided education first (see Chapter Two) and simply worked the crowd to let them know I was not going to shrink their heads or any such nonsense. Each trip became progressively easier and on the third trip when I walked into the room, people actually smiled and welcomed me! It was a hard battle just to gain an ounce of credibility. By the end of my work on this incident, however, the first responders were very receptive and open. It took tons of diligence, tenacity, and thick skin on my part, and a willingness on their part to try again to trust me, but we finally reached the end state of healing and moving forward. So much more work had been created by bad interventions; it took months to undo the damage.

The bottom line is this: Put resources and a plan in place. No first responders should have to suffer and go through their careers unable to access good care. Besides Kumbaya Queen, I have been called Shrink,

Hug Squad, Warrior Healer (my favorite), and The Wizard. Whatever you call me is fine. I will answer to anything, as long as you ask for and get help.

Chapter 2
Educate, Educate, Educate!

I'm going to change history
Enlighten the world
Teach them how to see through my eyes

"Lift Me Up" by Five Finger Death Punch, featuring
Rob Halford

The most important first step of appropriate care **before trauma occurs** is to educate, and keep educating, your most valuable resource—your people. It is the first and most important step on every syllabus in every academy, class, and initial training on dealing with trauma. You must know how to educate your personnel on the types of stress they will experience in their careers and effective ways to combat it. A stellar presentation is mandatory. One of the best things I've done in my career has been to develop a strong, poignant, and relevant brief to deliver to my customers. The feedback is consistently positive because the brief flows and makes sense. When a Sergeant Major in the United States Marine Corps declares in a written evaluation that this is the best brief he has seen in twenty years, you know you are on point. When a Lance Corporal from the Marine Corps sends you an email from Iraq stating how everything taught in his pre-deployment brief is exactly right and that he knows how to manage his deployment because he saw the brief, you know you're dead on.

Briefing your staff before, during, and after trauma is imperative. Pre-incident briefs arm recipients with knowledge and understanding of what to expect, that what happens is completely normal and nothing to be ashamed of, and it allows them the opportunity to plan for how they will mitigate the resulting stress. It also reassures them that getting help is good, often necessary, and it's what we do.

During a traumatic event, ongoing briefs are great for many reasons. It keeps responders informed when a person of authority connected with the incident, such as a supervisor, can update them. It mitigates rumors and gives clinicians and peer support the ability not only to educate on normal reactions, but also the ability to help affected personnel understand what lies ahead. It allows for the ability to define traumatic grief and to educate personnel on the emotional roller coaster they may experience during trauma. Reminding people to stay hydrated and nourished are all key factors in assuring the path to recovery can begin. It also highlights the fact that support is available and, after a good brief, first responders are much more likely to reach out to available support.

One of the most important aspects of the brief is it builds credibility and trust at a time when first responders are guarded, hurting, even afraid to speak their minds and share what is going on for them. I never, ever, walk up to a brand-new group or agency and expect them to open up. As a matter of fact, I speak first. I teach. I normalize. Then I open things up to discussion if they so choose. Asking a bunch of strong, alpha types to open up and talk first is a definitive setup for failure.

Some of the most remarkable agencies I work with are the ones that have brought me in because a horrific trauma has occurred. Each and every time I walk into a group like this, I am operating at ground zero of credibility. If they have already had poorly conducted debriefings, I'm not even at ground zero—I'm in the red. I start that brief slowly, and steadily climb my way out of the hole of zero credibility, and I do it by speaking the language of first responders and by using pertinent examples they can connect with. I also apply just the right amount of humor if appropriate. Sometimes humor is appropriate, and sometimes you leave it out.

If you know your audience—if you get good background information going into a brief and you can "read" them as you go in—you will deliver the right brief. I worked a significantly traumatic helicopter crash and as soon as I saw my audience (about thirty-six hours after the crash), I immediately hid a few of my slides. I could tell by the thousand-yard stares and traumatized facial expressions that they had had very little sleep, their attention spans were tanked, and they could not comprehend much more than a twenty-minute brief. The brief I delivered was to-the-point and exactly what they needed. I know this because, as soon as I was done, the flight crews asked me to develop their recovery plan for the path ahead. They put their faith in me to guide them after a pertinent and well-delivered brief. Know your audience. Listen to your folks. Trust your gut.

At the end of a traumatic incident, a good brief is a fantastic way to tie everything together. First responders have a chance to reflect on how far they have come since day one of the incident, what the sticking points are in their recovery, and how to combat any long-term detrimental effects of trauma.

However, just giving the brief is not enough. You have to mean it—really sell it. You have to love giving it, and your passion needs to come through. With this population, you have to have cool pictures and relevant stories to highlight concepts. If you don't have the passion, don't bother giving a brief. Public servants will walk away and comment this was "just another bullshit touchy-feely stress brief." If that happens, your mission has not been accomplished. Worse, you have turned responders off to accepting future briefs and being open to getting help. This is bad, bad, bad.

The Brief

"I seriously thought I was losing it, and I'd lost all my nerve." These were the words spoken to me recently after a briefing on the fight-or-flight response.

The place to start in a stress/trauma brief is normalizing the stress response by linking it to the fight-or-flight response that's engrained in all of us. Every public safety professional understands this concept, and when the four types of stress are connected to the fight-or-flight response, it normalizes and validates all their reactions. This is how to grab their attention and keep it. We all need the fight-or-flight response to survive. It is the awesome, kick-butt, and amazing human response that allows us to do things we never thought we could. When you set fight or flight at the foundation of stress, it removes the whole "touchy feely" weakness climate that often exists in stress briefs and that can turn off your audience.

In a fight-or-flight response, our brain activates our bodies to produce copious amounts of adrenaline, glucose, and cortisol. This response is all about strength, lasting in the fight, and blocking pain—it is all about survival and nothing else. The difference between fight and flight is a choice your brain makes. If you are walking in the woods and a mama bear, who happens to be spending a nice day with her cub, would like to speak with you, you are not going to fight with her. It's time to go! One of my SWAT teams told me they thought flight meant cowardice. The choice to flee has nothing to do with cowardice; sometimes the best choice for survival is to retreat and re-attack when backup arrives. Your brain is making a good decision—kill now, kill later, or be killed. It's really quite simple.

After acknowledging this basic foundation of the stress reaction, it's imperative to link fight or flight as a common thread in the four types of stress: acute stress, delayed stress, cumulative stress, and post-traumatic stress disorder.

Acute stress is also called incident-prompted stress. It begins on-scene or within twenty-four hours and is very obvious because there are many physiological reactions that are overt and uncomfortable. Acute stress responses occur after responders are involved in an overwhelming incident, their coping mechanisms are overwhelmed, and they have launched into fight or flight. There are a series of normal reactions evident with acute stress responses, and it's important that the normalization of these reactions is consistently mentioned. Signs of acute stress responses include:

1. Shaking—the cortisol triggers your circulation to divert your blood flow to your body's core in order to oxygenate the heart, lungs, and major muscles in your back, arms, and legs for running power and striking power. This is called shunting. Also, with decreased circulation, you are less likely to bleed to death if you are cut during a fight. When you couple shunting with adrenaline raging through your system, the side effect is shaking or trembling.

2. Throwing up—when you launch into fight or flight, you stop digesting because digestion burns too many calories that can be used for the fight. You don't need the food in your belly, so your system triggers you to get rid of it. Also, if you offload the weight in your belly, you are lighter so you can run faster.

3. Loss of bladder and bowel control—if your bladder is punctured or your bowel is eviscerated and the urine or feces go all over you, the long-term issue is that you will go septic. Your brain instructs your body to get rid of this possible health threat.

4. Prefrontal cortex shutdown—when your heart rate jumps to 180 to 220 beats per minute, it triggers your prefrontal cortex to shut down. This is the thinking, reasoning, analyzing, decision-making, and standard-operating-procedure-remembering portion of your brain. When that shuts off, the midbrain kicks on: this is the animal portion in all of us—kill or be killed. So, we kill.

In 2006, I was doing quite a bit of work with the Fourth Marine Division as they deployed to and returned from the wars in Iraq and Afghanistan. It was a very stressful time for the military, as it seemed that every day between 2005 and 2007 was a bad day. The war was full of chaos and the danger was at its highest levels. The insurgency was strong and the use of terror tactics was at an all-time high. I was giving a brief to five hundred Marines who were four days from deployment to Iraq, and they were extremely stressed. The hardest part was the wait, as the pre-deployment time seemed to drag on. Most Marines just wanted to get the heck out so they could get to the mission. After one of the briefs, a Marine told me my slide on acute stress was extremely useful and helped him understand that he was normal. He went on to explain that he had had an acute stress response during his first deployment and he now understood why. I asked him to tell me his story. Here it is:

This Marine was on a convoy and at the end of the convoy were three Humvees. He was in the third Humvee. There was an abandoned vehicle on the side of the road, and they did not have good intelligence on that vehicle. He maintained that they were very concerned and tried repeatedly to get more information on it, but were unsuccessful. They had a bad feeling, but they rolled on. As his Humvee passed the abandoned vehicle—the first two Humvees had passed without incident—the vehicle exploded with a force he had never felt before. The force of the explosion flipped their Humvee over. When he opened his eyes, the first thing he noticed was that the two junior Marines with him were dead. He saw a Marine in the second Humvee "puke all over the place." He self-extricated from his Humvee, took his rifle, and charged to the burning, exploding vehicle. I will never forget this part of the story. He said, "I had my rifle and I started circling that burning vehicle and I kept getting as close as I could without catching on fire. It was so hot and, honestly, if I could have climbed in the fire, I would have. I was in a rage to find the asshole who did this, and to kill him... but it doesn't really make sense, does it? If he was in the vehicle, he was gone. If he was two blocks away with his chicken-shit detonator, he was gone. But it made perfect sense to me at the time because I just wanted to find him and kill him." At this point, I asked what happened next. He replied, "The Marines from the second Humvee ran over and grabbed me and pulled me behind their vehicle, and I puked everywhere. I've always wondered why I did all that. Now I know. It was an acute stress response, and it was normal. Thank you."

How do you respond to something like that? I looked straight at this Marine and said, "No, thank you. For all you have done and are about to do."

Delayed stress is basically an acute stress reaction days, weeks, or even months after an event. The reason for the delay is because we "numb out" really well and take control during an incident. When the numbing wears off or the brain is ready to deal with it, responders and military members are punched with a delayed stress reaction. The delayed stress reaction is disturbing because it feels as though it comes out of nowhere. People who experience delayed stress reactions often think they are fine—good to go—and then, BAM! I always encourage folks to understand that this is normal and it's simply now time to deal with the event. The key is to reach out for help and take that help.

One of the best examples of a delayed stress reaction in my career involved a helicopter pilot after a crash. His crash was purely mechanical, and he did an excellent job landing the aircraft. He walked away from the crash because years of experience and a tremendous amount of skill enabled him to land skillfully and safely. This pilot had peer support right away, and they did an excellent job meeting his immediate needs. He was grateful to them as he began to recover from his back injury. The peer support team was able to connect me to this pilot a few days after the crash, when he was resting and recovering at home. The conversation went like this.

Pilot: "Tania, I appreciate the call, but I really don't need you. I'm fine. I'm an excellent pilot. As a matter of fact, this crash wasn't my fault; it was purely mechanical and I crashed that thing with as much control as humanly possible (to the tune of $3 million) and I really don't care because I am an excellent pilot, and it wasn't my fault."

Me: "I am glad you're OK. I wanted to talk—" (I get cut off.)

Pilot: "Tania, again, I really am fine. I'm an awesome pilot. I did my job. I don't need you. I'm cool. As a matter of fact, I'm so cool that last night I had dinner with my ex-wife AND my girlfriend. Who has dinner with their ex-wife *and* their girlfriend? I do. Because I'm cool. I don't need you."

Me: "OK, but—" (I get cut off again.)

Pilot: "Thanks for the call. If I need you, I know how to reach you."

Me: "OK, take care."

Nine weeks later, my phone rings and it's the pilot. He proceeds to tell me he realizes I was trying to tell him something, that he was fine at the time and didn't need me—but he needs me now. I asked him what happened and his explanation was a classic delayed stress example.

The pilot was at his girlfriend's house, still recovering from his back injury. They were on the back porch playing cards, relaxing, when an air medical helicopter began circling overhead, waiting for a landing zone to be cleared. As it was circling above the house, the pilot described a feeling of suddenly being overwhelmed. He stated that the longer he listened to the helicopter circling above, the more he became convinced that the engine was going to die and that the helicopter would crash. He described what he thought was a panic attack and stated that he could not fathom getting back in the cockpit again.

The first thing I told this pilot was that he was having a delayed stress reaction. I explained that the panic feeling was a fight-or-flight response because the last time he was in a helicopter it was frightening and he got hurt, and his brain is telling him it's time to deal with the event. The numbing has worn off and the fight-or-flight reaction is his brain trying to protect him, because it now associates helicopters with crashes. I also told him we could address this and get him back to feeling normal. (More on trauma treatment and what I did for him in Chapter Four).

Cumulative stress is burnout. The key to managing burnout is to stay healthy and to have a life outside the job. Stay hydrated, nourished, and rested. Take care of family and financial issues. Get regular check-ups. Keep your faith, friends, hobbies, and fun in your life, and not just your work friends, but all others. Step out of your comfort zone: attend church, go to your kids' school plays, and cheer them on at their baseball games! In other words, have balance in life. First responders with healthy balance are less likely to experience burnout and are generally more resilient.

Post-traumatic stress disorder is at the farthest end of the spectrum of the stress continuum and most public safety professionals and military members fear that it will end their careers. Later in this book, there is much more information on PTSD, as this is my specialty and my passion. In the brief, however, it is extremely important to explain PTSD simply and clearly and address options for recovery. Here is the explanation I give in my briefs, and while this is simplified and condensed, the most important thing is to normalize this syndrome and provide hope that things can and will improve.

- PTSD is the end result of exposure to a stress trauma so extreme it is beyond human coping capacity. This response and its severity are different for everyone. For example, two individuals may have experienced the same trauma and one will indicate it was the worst thing he has ever seen, while the other states it was no big deal. It boils down to interpretation and what your brain considers traumatic.

- You take in information through your five senses; what you see, hear, taste, touch, and smell enters the frontal lobe of your brain. Normal information gets processed across the synapses in your brain and downloaded into your memory— short-term or long-term—depending on relevance.

- Trauma and traumatic information gets stored in your frontal lobe, which acts as a firewall for trauma and does not allow your brain to process it—it's simply too overwhelming.

- Over time, your frontal lobe attempts to push the information into your memory, but if it's too traumatic, it simply can't do so without assistance.

- As the frontal lobe attempts to download the traumatic memory, it causes the individual to re-experience the event over and over again. Each time this happens, it causes distress and a subsequent fight-or-flight response.

- Over time, the fight-or-flight response happens so many times that the cortisol it produces crosses the blood-brain barrier and hijacks the limbic system.

- Cortisol causes the hippocampus, which manages trauma and loss, to shrink.

- When the hippocampus shrinks, the amygdala essentially becomes hijacked by the damage to the brain. The amygdala is the gatekeeper to the fight-or-flight reaction. This mechanism decides when it's time to set the survival response in motion and when everything is fine and safe. When the amygdala is damaged, it always defaults to fight or flight rather than safe because otherwise we would not survive during danger.

- When the amygdala is damaged and defaults to fight or flight, it is no longer able to understand that you're fine. A car backfiring takes you right back to that firefight you were in. It doesn't care about logic. There is no timeline in the limbic system. All it knows is danger and how to set you in motion to stay alive.

- PTSD is essentially your survival mechanism in the wrong loop or cycle.

- The hippocampus is very "plastic." It heals by generating new neural pathways, and this is how we conquer PTSD. There are very effective techniques to realign the limbic system by opening these neural pathways. My favorite happens to be Eye Movement Desensitization and Reprocessing (EMDR). I explain EMDR in my briefs (more on that later).

The final necessary element of a good brief is effective stress management strategies. I always tell folks to go back to the basics of self-care. Eat right, stay hydrated, get rest, take naps, moderate alcohol intake, keep your family close and communicate with them as much as you can, practice your faith, and enjoy your hobbies. I discourage the abuse of painkillers and sleeping pills. I warn that, after trauma, the likelihood of someone getting a DWI/DUI increases significantly. I encourage safe and positive choices. I also tell responders to be aware of the "one-week and two-week marks." At one week post-incident, I want those images beginning to fade and for the telltale constant replay of the event to be slowing down. At two weeks post-incident, I want those images to seem as though they have "faded" and are stored in long-term memory. They're not pleasant, but individuals sense they have moved forward and regained a sense of control.

One of the most important aspects of every brief is to help responders feel normal, validated, and clear about getting help and staying healthy. A well-delivered and well-timed brief is essential. I literally have watched traumatized groups of first responders transform from angry, hostile, and skeptical, to engaged, hopeful, and positive in the course of a well-delivered brief. Use pictures. Give examples. Don't make stuff up. And for goodness' sake, stop talking about feelings! Make the brief about the biology of the stress response and focus on solutions. Again, stop talking about feelings!

One of my favorite clients is a police department in Texas. I was brought on with the department one month after an extremely horrific and tragic line-of-duty death of a patrol officer who also served as a SWAT operator. These officers were initially placed in critical incident briefings facilitated by those with good intentions, but some very serious mistakes were made. The group was expected to sit in a circle and open up and share their feelings. I will share my thoughts on this strategy in Chapter Three. They were also not triaged properly and officers who were off duty were placed in the same debriefing as those who performed chest compressions on the fallen officer. Needless to say, the officers not only deemed these debriefings as not helpful, every officer I spoke to when I was brought on said these debriefings made things worse for them. This is absolutely unacceptable. This gets a capital "F" for Failure.

I was brought in one month after the incident through word of mouth. When the assistant chief called me, I will never forget the expression he used. He indicated things were "unraveling." That summed it up. Things were really unraveling for these officers, and they were floundering. They had no clear sense of direction, and many were developing PTSD.

My first day with them was tricky. It's all about delivery. This was one of the situations in which I had to climb my way out of the credibility hole I was already in because of what I do and due to the ineffective interventions they had already received.

I arrived early and received a full brief regarding the events that had occurred. I asked to visit the scene so I could get a sense of where everyone was. I was shocked to find how tight everything was in terms of the proximity of the buildings, the shooter, and the officers. I spent time looking at the fragments, bullet holes, and got an overall feel for the area. Then I returned to the police department and presented a brief for the SWAT team.

The team walked into the room and sat in the back two rows with their arms crossed. They were angry and fed up. They were hurting. They already hated me. I had nothing but respect and care for them, and I communicated this to them the best I could from the start. The assistant chief mentioned in my introduction that I had already been to the scene. This sparked some interest. I also had my service dog with me, which engaged the team as she started to "work the crowd." I started the brief by explaining the fight-or-flight response. I addressed the types of stress and stress management strategies in terms of warrior resilience and staying in the fight. I referenced previous experiences. I talked about the disasters I had worked. At the end, I addressed solutions for trauma recovery. I asked if there were any questions. One officer raised his hand and asked if he could make an appointment that afternoon. My answer—of course! After the brief,

I was surrounded by SWAT team members: Can you visit the officer, who is still wounded and too weak to leave his home? Can you come to our training tomorrow? Can we set up appointments? Yes, yes, yes. Let's move forward. We can fight this together. And we did. This team went through a subsequent line-of-duty death ten months after the first one. This time, though, I was there with them through the entire thing. From start to finish, I was there to provide water, food, hugs, to dry tears, and then assist with the prevention of PTSD. They knew what to do that time, and we did it together. We fight this together.

Chapter 3
Triage and Intervene—But Do It Right!

When the fire's at my feet again
And the vultures all start circling
They're whispering "You're out of time"
But still I rise

"State of Mine" by Rise

The model I have developed for crisis intervention with first responders is what I call TEN FOUR. The acronym stands for: Triage–Educate–Normalize–Free dialogue–Organize thoughts–Understand the big picture–Restore resilience.

Peer support and crisis teams are responsible for the first portion of this model, TEN. Initial triaging of personnel is a must, followed by effective education and normalization of symptoms. This leads to the second component, FOUR, which first responders will start to do naturally as education and normalization begin. Education, followed by the opportunity to speak freely and casually, without pressure, leads to first responders organizing their thoughts, seeing the big picture, and working to restore their natural resilience that they rely on every day.

Triage

The first step in providing interventions is to triage the involved personnel and to constantly reevaluate based on what has occurred. The act of triaging is one of the most important components in service delivery. You cannot respond to any critical incident or disaster without it! Caring for people is not a one-size-fits-all service. Understanding who needs what and when is imperative. Without good triaging, you are setting up the response plan for total failure, potentially harming your employees. It is simply unacceptable.

Public safety folks who are in the midst of chaos have a very different experience and mindset after an incident than those who arrived later. The most frequent mistake made by clinicians and critical incident teams who respond to incidents is that they get in a hurry and decide to use one or two interventions for everyone. The result is that responders who were directly impacted are placed into the same intervention as responders who arrived later, when the situation was under control. The intervention thus fails all of the participants. Rescuers who are severely trauma-tized are not interested in hearing from someone who had a minimal role.

An example of such a mistake: a debriefing for personnel involved in managing a horrendous crash that included the deaths of several children. The de-briefing was mandatory for all personnel involved— police, fire, EMS, and communications. First off, the group was too big and chairs were set up in a circle (we will discuss this momentarily). The first person to speak was a paramedic who had been directly in-volved. He spoke at length and in detail about his ef-forts at pediatric CPR, including the fact that there was blood up to his elbows, a horrific scene. He talked about it just as he had been asked to do by the critical incident team. The next person to speak was a police officer, who stated that his job had been to di-rect traffic away from the scene two blocks away. He made it clear that he knew it was a bad wreck, but had not seen anything. He thanked the debriefing team for the opportunity to now have the images described firmly stuck in his mind. Result: a capital "F" Failure. There was absolutely no triaging, and when you don't triage, you make things worse.

How to Triage

The first thing I explain to teams is never, ever, to be in a hurry. There is no reason to rush. Take time to get your fingers on the emotional pulse of everyone involved. It will give you a feel of what to do and when to do it. Take the time to meet everyone and to get a really good brief on what actually happened (not what you saw on the news). Get a sense of how the organizations involved are responding, including to the fact that help has arrived.

Once you are ready to start triaging and implementing intervention, make sure you keep it simple. I like to use a target analogy, with a bull's-eye in the middle and rings surrounding the bull's-eye.

In the center of the bull's-eye are the first responders who were directly involved. This means the ones who were right there when it happened or were the first to arrive. In the event that those who were in the bull's-eye are deceased or seriously injured, the bull's-eye will include those who were first on the scene. If responders are seriously injured, their mental health care must begin as soon as reasonable or possible, but may have to be delayed until physical recovery is underway.

Communications specialists involved in the incident are always in the bull's-eye. Never make the mistake of thinking that just because they were not present, they are fine or less impacted. Communications personnel can be just as traumatized, if not more so, than personnel on scene. They have no visual references and rely solely on what they hear. They create pictures in their minds. The overwhelming emotional experience for communications personnel, therefore, is utter helplessness, an experience extremely damaging to the human psyche.

From the bull's-eye, you move to the first ring. The first ring consists of team members who arrived next and who are often directly impacted, as well. As you move out to each ring, think in terms of who responded next, who was on duty at the time and, while they heard about it, they did not respond. And finally, personnel who were off duty at the time.

As you identify the personnel that fall into each area of the target, you can begin to plan your interventions based on what each group needs. The key to good triaging is this: While you can't always prevent the blurring of some of the lines, it is important to keep the groups with similar or homogeneous experiences as separate as possible. This means that it is imperative not to debrief personnel in the bull's-eye together with personnel who were off duty. Their experiences are drastically different, as are the ranges of reactions. Once you have a good sense of folks involved and their level of exposure, it is time to implement interventions.

The First Steps

The first thing I want to mention when discussing interventions is that I always prefer to have peer support with me. If I am with an organization that does not utilize peer support, my work is much harder. I train peer support in these interventions so we can work as a team or divide and conquer if we need to.

It is important in the aftermath of a crisis to remain focused on crisis resolution. The human brain is an amazingly powerful thing, and it is designed to heal and resolve trauma, but we all need assistance from time to time in getting past that trauma. The point of crisis intervention is to stabilize, normalize, and assist personnel in bouncing back in a healthy manner.

When I teach peer support and crisis intervention classes, the phrase "be a human being first" is repeated multiple times. In other words, how would you want to be treated if you were in that person's shoes? Asking first responders to let down their walls, allow us to intervene, and maybe, just maybe, to trust us is asking a lot of highly trained, tough responders who are expected to be in control at all times. We are asking first responders to go against what is generally their first inclination—to bottle up, stuff, or ignore their trauma—and give us the chance to walk them through it instead. This delivery is very, very important.

By teaching my students to be human beings first, I ask them to look at Maslow's Hierarchy of Needs. At the base of the hierarchy are the basics of human survival: food, water, clothing, and shelter. I believe safety belongs at the base, as well, because human beings can only survive with fear for so long before their psychological well-being is damaged.

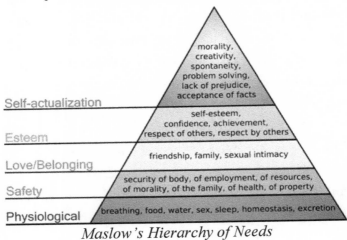

Maslow's Hierarchy of Needs

When responding to a crisis, one of the best and most logical things to do first is to show up with food, water, sports drinks, blankets, and pillows—whatever the affected persons need. The message is very clear: we care about you, we have brought things to make you comfortable, and we are very focused on what you need. The usual expectation when a crisis team shows up is that they are going to make everyone uncomfortable and force them to talk. When you show up with armfuls of gifts, it lets people know that this is not the case.

The next step is to simply take the time to assist. A group of first responders will explain that, due to their schedule disruption, they are now dealing with child care issues, or they need to get home to let their pets outside, or they are overdue to pick up a spouse or a parent, and so forth. Traumatic events always represent major disruptions to the lives of those who are impacted. The most logical and meaningful thing to do is to help. Drive people to where they need to be, help them coordinate the tasks they must accomplish. To ignore this is to tell them that their priorities do not matter. This is simply wrong. Jump in and help out. The message is, "We are here to help, however that might be." These acts of kindness will pay off monumentally in building credibility and trust.

Early in my career, I was called out to assist multiple EMTs and paramedics after a very significant crash involving a church van and a pickup truck. The church van was full of children and was flipped on its side. The pickup truck had spun into a field, was very difficult to see, and not found for quite some time. One of the occupants of the pickup truck was a woman who was celebrating her forty-fifth birthday. Her husband had been driving her to a surprise birthday party. She was pronounced dead at the scene. Along with that, seven children from the van—all fatally and drastically wounded—were pronounced dead on the scene. It was a horrible accident.

Communications called and asked me to head to the EMS station, where the crews were gathering. When I arrived, they were busy scrubbing blood off their bunker gear and restocking their ambulances. As I walked up the driveway, I recognized that they were not ready for me and noticed that they started to hurry up to finish. I approached and asked them not to hurry, because we had all the time they needed. I also told them they probably wouldn't want me to restock the ambulances because I was sure to mess that up, but I could help scrub the bunker gear. We spent the next thirty minutes cleaning and restocking. When we went into the station, they started to hurry again, thinking they were imposing on my time. As they sat down, I noticed they were all sweating, and many of them needed a uniform change. I explained that it was more important for them to get comfortable first. I asked them to hydrate, change clothes, call home—whatever they needed to do. Once all that was done, then we were ready. These simple acts mean so much to first responders. When a crew is clean, ready, and comfortable, and not worried about being unprepared for the next call, I have their full attention. Interventions are much more effective when personnel are ready to receive them.

Educate and Normalize

As stated in Chapter Two, it all begins with education. First responders in a crisis are rarely inclined to simply open up and start talking. Every agency, organization, department—every customer and every client—gets education first. I do this every time I begin working with a customer and this means I educate the entire department. To be sure, it is labor intensive and usually involves several briefs, but the payoff is huge. Educating accomplishes a lot of things: it introduces people to me, and me to them. They know who is coming and what to expect. It provides continuing education units. It normalizes and educates first responders. It serves as a pre-incident inoculation and gets them ready for their next incident. It teaches them the terminology I will use after a crisis. It allows them to understand what to expect from me. It assists in their realization that there is a source for help, an outlet to deal with events that might have been ignored previously.

In the aftermath of a crisis, after the stabilization of individuals, I always teach first. Whether I have the luxury of time and am able do a brief with a PowerPoint or I just have a few minutes in which I need to simply address the next few steps ahead, I always teach first. It assures everyone we are going to take things one step at a time, they are not crazy, and they are going to get through this event.

How much and how long I teach is based on tri-aging the impacted group. I have several PowerPoint briefs of various lengths to use at any time; what has happened and how people are responding determine the length of the brief I will use. That said, I have to tell you, I have walked into situations where I hid my slides because I knew I had too much information for the impacted personnel. And I have walked into situations where the thumb drive in my pocket was never taken out and instead I just talked to the responders.

The most important things is to look at and listen to your people, to know what they are capable of absorbing. The more drastic the incident and the closer the time to the incident, the less they will retain. When you see thousand-yard stares, understand that their attention span is probably about three minutes. Assess your people and trust your gut. This is not your show—it is theirs.

As previously mentioned, I did extensive work with a SWAT team after a graphic, violent, horrible line-of-duty death. I was brought in one month after the event and, while they were angry and traumatized, they had basically survived the first month and were relatively focused. I spent about two hours presenting their brief since they could focus, and also because I needed the time to build credibility and obtain buy-in through delivering the brief.

I also mentioned some of the air medical crashes I have worked. On one incident, I was brought in about thirty-six hours after the crash. This was a time I had planned to use a slide deck. But when the impacted individuals walked into the room, I could tell they were overwhelmed, traumatized, and very fatigued. I knew immediately that I needed to shorten the duration based on the way they looked, so I hid some of the slides right before the presentation.

Then there are the instances when you simply need to scrap the slides and speak from your heart to engage your customers and begin to help them stabilize. In 2015, I had two customers who had line-of-duty deaths—one flight nurse and one police officer, both of whom worked in small, close-knit organizations. Their deaths impacted everyone strongly, due to the size of the programs they came from, as well as how they died. In both events, I was there within a few hours and it was clear that all personnel needed guidance, support, compassion, and love.

When these circumstances occur, I simply speak to what is relevant. I address issues to include traumatic grief, the emotional roller coaster after a line-of-duty death, what to expect in the first two weeks, the importance of self-care, healthy stress management, how to talk to family members about what has happened, and the importance of refraining from drinking and driving. I always address this last point, as organizations are more likely to experience this problem in the aftermath of a line-of-duty death.

Each time I brief impacted personnel, as we move further away from the event in duration, I build on what I have already addressed and add new topics, such as preparing for the funeral, how to address the family members of the deceased, ways to organize and help out with the arrangements, the many things that occur after the event, and what to expect during the grieving process.

During the initial briefs, when everyone is in shock and things are very raw, it is possible to pull larger groups together or entire teams together to educate without specifically triaging with the target model. The reason is that you are providing information and answering questions. The task is simply to stabilize and inform. This is the only time, however, that minimal triaging can be done.

Free Dialogue

As things begin to calm down, it is time to move from general educational briefs to emotional processing briefs. These must be handled very carefully. Triaging here is a must. It is imperative to pull the homogenous groups together for these.

Mitchell and Everly (1996) created the very first model that addressed public safety emotional care during the 1980s. The Critical Incident Stress Management (CISM) model took hold and has been widely practiced for many years. While I see the value in the model and the way they teach it, I have modified it over the years to make it stronger and more user-friendly.

I first noticed during our deployment to the Murrah Federal Building bombing in Oklahoma City in 1995 that the CISM process had some strong limitations. The first had to do with the initial things teams were instructed to do at the beginning—to put the chairs in a circle. I completely and wholeheartedly disagreed with this concept. If you have ever done it, I am sure you noticed you quickly lose first responders as they walk in the door. When they see the chairs in a circle, you have instant resistance. First responders will make angry remarks about group therapy or the fact that they didn't realize they were attending an Alcoholics Anonymous meeting. Their discomfort is visible at the outset, and it remains that way throughout the process. The other implication is the fact that to get the chairs in a circle, you may be moving furniture in a place where first responders report for duty, such as a "show up," or you may be rearranging furniture in their second home (their station, firehouse, etc.). First responders are frequently superstitious about their routines. They do the same things before every shift, sit in the same spot, and begin their shifts with a certain sequence of activities. This is largely due to the fact that for many of them, the one time that their routine is disrupted may turn out to have been the worst shift of their careers so far. I do not advocate moving their furniture—ever.

Another limitation of the CISM process is the awkwardness of the questions posed during the debriefing process. It became obvious to me very early on in my career that first responders really prefer and do much better with a casual conversation. Having the gift of gab and engaging in a process that feels more like "cussing and discussing" is a much easier way to conduct interventions. Let's face it—we all have war stories and when someone simply asks, "What happened out there?" it's much easier to share those details in a conversational style than in a formal, structured style with questions designed to probe.

To engage the group in the free-dialogue phase, I educate first and simply open it up to discussion by asking the group one or two questions about what has occurred. When groups of first responders are comfortable, they will talk. Sometimes they will sit around and "shoot the breeze" for hours. I usually pass out snacks when this happens. They are on a roll and want to stay and talk. But sometimes first responders simply don't want to talk. There may be dynamics in the group that we are not aware of or pending investigations, when they've been told by attorneys not to say anything. This is their right, as well. The bottom line is, they have better education and tools to begin to deal with the event. They also have names and contact numbers to follow up with later.

Organize Thoughts and Understand the Big Picture

Starting with the bull's-eye in every situation, the peer support team and I will pull those folks together, and after we have covered our role and confidentiality, we educate first. If they have already had some education from us, we build on what we have taught them and educate further. At this point, we open the conversation up to a very informal discussion, in which we essentially ask the first responders to share whatever they are comfortable with. The participants can discuss what occurred, ask questions, or simply vent. It is very informal and easygoing. I do not refer to it as a defusing or a debriefing, I simply refer to it as a brief or briefing. We keep it simple, low-key, and casual. At the end of each brief, we hand out a brochure that normalizes stress reactions and encourages positive coping skills. What happens in these moments of the process is amazing. First responders have the chance to share their perspectives and, for the first time for many of them, they begin to gain insight into what actually happened, they see the entire big picture, and many of the missing puzzle pieces start to come together. First responders typically walk away from this information-sharing with a much clearer picture of the event and a different perspective. The shift in perspective is based on new information and insight, and this usually means they can understand just how severe the situation was. They realize how little control there was and what they were able to do to regain control. This often means closure for most first responders.

From the bull's-eye we move outward, ring by ring, and repeat the process until we are done. As impacted personnel come through the brief, they respond well when it is done correctly. They then tell their colleagues it was helpful, and generally, each brief gets progressively easier due to increased accumulated credibility.

Restore Resilience

As we go through the process, I prefer to keep things real. I hear all the time that first responders who went through a critical incident in the past were told to exercise, avoid alcohol, eat healthy, and avoid caffeine. I don't think this is realistic or appropriate. People are going to do what they do, which might mean eat comfort food or drink a lot of caffeine because they are tired. What I always tell people is, during the aftermath of a terrible incident, it's important to take care of yourself. Go back to the basics of self-care. This means stay hydrated, eat when you can, moderate the alcohol if you are willing, and try to get sleep. If your sleep is disrupted by this trauma, take naps during the day. Try to spend time with your family. Do the things you enjoy. Exercise if you are inclined to do so. Take your vitamins and consider adding extra vitamins C, D, and zinc to get you through this tough time. Ask for help.

Throughout the entire process, we are always assessing how personnel are doing. The peer support team and I make ourselves available for one-on-one time whenever someone wants that. The more time you spend with a group of first responders, the more they will seek out this type of assistance. Peer support members are carefully vetted and trained to listen and guide first responders in problem-solving and healthy coping. They are also aware of what is beyond their capabilities, and they know when it is time to encourage a first responder to see a clinician.

The most challenging aspect of intervening with first responders is the resistance you will meet. Whether this is due to the culture or the fact that they have been through poorly run interventions in the past, you should expect it each and every time you respond to an incident. The key to resolving this is to avoid making it seem like an intervention, but more like extended family showing up to help out any way you can. Pulling this off takes patience, compassion, and strong attention to details. But it works. And it's amazing to watch the transformation of impacted personnel back to healthy and happy.

Mitchell, Jeffrey T. & Everly, George S. *Critical Incident Stress Debriefing: An Operations Manual for CISD, Defusing and Other Group Crisis Intervention Services.* 3rd Edition (Columbia, Maryland: Chevron Publishing, 1996).

Chapter 4

PTSD: We Fight This Together

Wake in a sweat again
Another day's been laid to waste
In my disgrace
Stuck in my head again
Feels like I'll never leave this place
There's no escape

"Given Up" by Linkin Park

In this chapter, my main goal is to help readers understand what PTSD really is and how we conquer it. There is much information available on post-traumatic stress disorder. As described in Chapter Two, PTSD is the result of being exposed to a stress trauma that is extreme and beyond a person's coping capacity. The event is usually sudden and unexpected, traumatic or graphic in nature, and to some degree violent. First responders are trained to take control of any situation and remain in control. Events that cause PTSD frequently feel as though control is lost. It is a very unsettling experience for first responders. No academy teaches "Helplessness 101." When it happens, it reverberates in people's minds and recovery is often very difficult.

For first responders who are exposed to trauma beyond their coping capacity, images, smells, and sounds are captured by the frontal lobes of their brains and lodge themselves there. The frontal lobe acts as a firewall for trauma. It captures the event because it cannot process it like normal information. When first responders are able to restore their natural functioning—usually when they go off shift or are at home— the frontal lobe will try to process this trauma. The frontal lobe attempts to process these sights and smells, and first responders experience this as reliving the event, thinking constantly about it, seeing the event as though it's a movie or like having nightmares.

For the first few days following such an event, it is quite normal to constantly replay it many times over. What I explain to first responders is this: by seven days after the incident, I want these images, smells, and sounds to seem like they are fading to long-term memory. It is normal to think about it quite a bit, but at one week post-incident I want the replay to slow down significantly. By fourteen days after the incident, I want that event lodged into long-term memory. You don't think about it constantly and the nightmares have stopped. You may never forget the event, but you definitely feel the difference between the first few days, when the event was in your face, to fourteen days later, when you have gained space and distance from it. If, after fourteen days, you are still experiencing those distressing sights, smells, and sounds, or if you are still having nightmares about the event, I want you to get help. Please do not stuff it, ignore it, walk it off, or drink it off. Get help immediately.

Over the course of time, when the frontal lobe cannot download or process those captured images into your long-term memory, the likelihood of the onset of post-traumatic stress disorder increases significantly. When this occurs, a damaged hippocampus (through copious release of glucocorticoids) and a "hijacked" amygdala create a perfect storm inside the brain. Individuals with PTSD have sudden, extreme attacks of reliving the events, which are constantly triggered by their environment, putting them in a constant state of fight or flight.

PTSD is overwhelming and debilitating. The result is that first responders with post-traumatic stress disorder will have difficulty performing their jobs. They will have difficulty in social situations or in public, and they will most likely begin to isolate themselves. Tasks such as going to the grocery store are beyond overwhelming. Forget about going to parties or on dates! First responders are now incapable of many things they used to take for granted. And, they are so ashamed and embarrassed by their condition that they just live on in misery. The hijacked amygdala tells a first responder to fight or run constantly. Living with PTSD is horrible for the individual and for their family members.

Contrary to what many public safety professionals think, PTSD is something we have solutions for. I refer to it as conquering the demons, and together we fight that good fight until my patients are well. In the early 1990s, Dr. Francine Shapiro stumbled upon the Eye Movement Desensitization and Reprocessing (EMDR) technique. As she began to develop and refine the technique, patients began to report significant improvements and even resolution of their PTSD. The research on EMDR, on the training and the evolution of the technique's application, has shown the best advancement in the treatment of PTSD by far, in my opinion. I was trained in the technique in 1995. Like most clinicians, I was unsure and even a little skeptical. My supervisor at the time indicated that the technique was amazing, well worth the time and money.

My first day of training was April 19, 1995. As we were about to take a break, one of the instructors informed the class there had been a bombing outside the Murrah Federal Building in Oklahoma City. I ran upstairs to my hotel room to watch the horror unfolding. I could not believe what I was seeing. I will never forget those images. I went back to class more motivated than ever. As fate would have it, my first real EMDR patient, two weeks after my training, was a first responder in Oklahoma City. He was an Oklahoma City firefighter who was totally traumatized by that horrific day. I explained the EMDR technique, and he responded very quickly with, "Let's do it." As I pulled up my chair to begin, I was having a mental conversation with myself: *Really? This is your first EMDR patient? Why do you do this to yourself?* I took a deep breath, remembered my EMDR training, said a quick prayer, and off we went. The result was amazing! No, actually phenomenal! I literally watched this hero transform from completely traumatized and desperate to get those images out of his mind to a completely relaxed, healthy, hopeful, and positive firefighter—all in the course of two hours. I met this firefighter's niece at a law enforcement spouse's conference a few years later. She told me her uncle had a long and happy career, he had recently retired because he was going to start losing money if he didn't, and he never experienced any PTSD. She went on to tell me he spoke to many about a girl named Tania from Texas who had fixed his brain. This is one of the many reasons I love EMDR.

The key to the EMDR process lies in the fact the brain is very resilient. EMDR is designed to process trauma; this technique taps into the brain's ability to heal itself. The process of replicating rapid eye movements triggers the frontal lobe to process those images and allows the brain to basically move them to long-term memory. The hippocampus generates new neural pathways in the process and actually heals as it creates these new pathways to process trauma. The technique is fast and effective. It's exhausting and usually generates a headache, but when you think about the tremendous amount of work being done by a brain as it heals itself, grows new neural pathways, and unlocks and processes trauma, it's understandable that a patient is basically wiped out after an EMDR session. In addition to the images being processed, the emotions attached to the event get processed, as well. The beauty is that first responders don't have to talk about their feelings while this is occurring. They certainly can if they want to, but if it makes them uncomfortable, they don't have to. Bottom line: trauma and associated reactions get processed very quickly. First responders tell me all the time they wish they had done EMDR sooner, they now have their lives back, and that the treatment has been their pathway out of PTSD hell.

I was trained the original way in EMDR, which involves the patient tracking my fingertips as I move them back and forth in equal, bilateral motions, about twelve inches from the patient's face. Since its inception, EMDR has added light bars, pulse pads, and headphones with tones to mimic the bilateral stimulation and to help therapists with the arm fatigue many experience. The original method, as labor intensive as it can be, is still my favorite way to practice. While there are several steps we take throughout the EMDR process, I try to keep it as smooth and free-flowing as possible. You can read about the steps involved in the technique online or in any EMDR book. While I go through all these steps in every EMDR session, my goal is to keep first responders moving through each step, without troubling them with explanations. In other words, it's important to make the process seem more like a path or a journey that first responders and the clinician are taking together.

The outcome of the EMDR session is nothing short of amazing. When those synapses open and the brain starts to process the trauma, first responders tend to remember suppressed details. These are usually positive details, such as what they did to assist others. Trauma is inherently negative—we always remember the bad—until we do EMDR. First responders also report that the pervasive, ugly images that have invaded their mind have faded. They describe the experience as gaining distance, fading, and even having a difficult time remembering it, or "seeing it," in their mind. The second part of this amazing process is the fact that patients will also notice that the very intense, negative emotions are gone. They describe being at peace with the event or just being "past it." As they discuss how they are responding so differently to the event after EMDR, they realize their perspective has changed. In other words, they usually realize they did everything they could in the situation or there was nothing more they could have realistically done. WOW!! For the first time ever after a trauma, first responders feel relief, and they actually are able to forgive themselves.

After EMDR, I send my patients home for a nap, and I ask them to take it easy. They often note they are tired and report they sleep well through the night. Because we have opened the synapses and the brain is firing away, I explain to my patients that this processing will typically continue for a day or two. This means many events from their lives and careers will be reprocessed. The experience is that the images float by rapidly. I ask my patients to take note of the images, but to expect them to be gone very quickly.

As a clinician, I always touch base with my clients the next day to see how they are doing and ask if they have any questions. I love hearing how significantly better they feel.

However, a traditional talk therapist will ask patients about their trauma, and as the patients begin to describe the horrible event that occurred, the therapist will ask first responders to further explore that moment. This occurs session after session and all the while, as first responders are pulling up that trauma, their amygdalas are telling them to fight or run. They sit in a therapist's office in full-blown fight-or-flight mode and they are miserable. Why would you want to do this to anyone? I tell my patients that the first ten to fifteen minutes of EMDR are difficult. I ask for their trust in getting them through it and I explain that once the brain starts to process those images, they are going to start to experience relief. I am not sure why anyone would put a PTSD survivor through talk therapy.

As a clinician, I will say that when I first started doing EMDR, I had to mentally catch up to my patients. They heal so quickly as their entire limbic systems get realigned, their hippocampus heals, and their amygdala stops firing all the time. I found myself behind the curve mentally with my patients, as they headed for discharge much sooner than normal. I became used to it after about a year, but it was quite an adjustment initially for me.

The other technique I like to do is progressive desensitization. I refer to EMDR and progressive desensitization as "the one-two punch" to PTSD. Progressive desensitization is the process of returning to the scene where something occurred, or to an activity that caused a trauma. After doing EMDR, I have taken my patients and returned to scenes of bad fires and traumatic accidents. I have taken confidence flights with flight crews. Several times I have driven through an intersection that was the scene of an accident with a first responder behind the wheel. After EMDR, we basically go out to the demons and bury them once and for all. This empowers first responders to do their jobs. It takes the mystery out of what it will feel like to go back to that place. It allows them to return to that location while on duty with no hesitation or worries. With veterans, progressive desensitization after EMDR consists of going to grocery stores, banks, restaurants—all the places they are avoiding. We walk and talk until they are at peace. It usually takes very little time, because after EMDR their brains are ready to return to normal. We talk about healthy situational awareness versus constant fight or flight. We talk about trusting their instincts again. After this is done, my patients are ready to get back to work, to the gym, the grocery store, or whatever they have been avoiding. The Now becomes possible again.

In no way am I saying that EMDR and progressive desensitization are the only techniques to treat post-traumatic stress disorder, but because they are so very effective and bring such relief, they are definitely my two favorite techniques. As we will discuss in Chapter Seven, first responders typically do not want to come to therapy, and when they do, they want issues resolved quickly. They are "fixers," as they fix problems all day long. They tend to expect the same from their therapists. The mantra of first responders coming to therapy is "Fix me yesterday."

After EMDR and progressive desensitization, I like to help my clients adjust to their new lives after the horrors of PTSD. For many, it involves getting used to new perspectives, their new routines without triggers, and making up for lost time spent isolating and not socializing with family and friends. I explain that after conquering trauma, life is like a new pair of shoes. They are excited about their new shoes, but soon understand those new shoes have to be broken in. A little uncomfortable at first, it takes some time getting used to their new shoes. Not having triggers, being in touch with your healthy instincts, being able to sleep, not having to avoid the public—these are all aspects of life first responders have to get used to again. The longer they have lived with their trauma, the more significant these changes will feel. It's fun to start living again, and it's even a little scary. I always tell first responders that if they can conquer trauma, they can certainly learn how to live their healthy lives again.

Jeremy's Story

Jeremy is a firefighter who had a near-death experience in a structure fire. When he started therapy, he was not sleeping, was extremely agitated, and had no idea how he would ever get through his trauma and get back to work. Not only did he return to work, he recently was promoted to captain. His leap of faith in EMDR resulted in a testimonial where he stated, "EMDR is the pathway out of hell." I am so proud of him. What follows is his story.

Can you tell me about your incident?

It was a Sunday morning and we were called to a condo fire with reports of someone trapped inside. I remember getting on scene and a lady saying that, because a certain car was in the parking lot, a woman was inside. She was reportedly an elderly woman who would not be able to get herself out. When we got up to the second floor of the condo, the living area was on fire. We were working with other crews and we were able to knock down the walls to see inside. We pushed through into the living room and did an initial search to see if we could find a body. At that point, given the fire circumstances, we knew that was all there would be.

At that time, my nozzleman said he wanted to swap. The line was being overpumped and it was hot. We switched up and as we did, the fireplace fell. The fireplace hit me and knocked me to the floor. I fell on my left side and was knocked unconscious. I came to and there was a hole in the floor on the other side of me. I could see through to the floor. And I could not find my nozzleman. At that time, I was thrown through the air like a ragdoll. I felt my feet give way. I came to rest buried by bricks from my left hip across to my right shoulder. My left arm and legs were buried. My right arm was free. I tried to radio for help, but couldn't get through on the radio. I could tell something was wrong with my neck and my back. I could feel my legs burning and I felt like I was being burned alive. I hit the emergency button on my radio.

I looked down and saw the top of a helmet. That's all I could see. Everything else was buried. I was able to free myself from debris to my waist, but I couldn't get any farther. I bent over and started digging toward the helmet, hoping my other firefighter was conscious. I got to his shoulders and his arms popped out. He started digging himself out. I called a mayday and got no response. I tried multiple times and the only person who ever answered was dispatch. I heard the commander give the call to pull everyone out of the structure.

At that moment, I felt abandoned. Dispatch tried to call him but got no answer. I felt like everyone was leaving, and I was being burned alive. I remember thinking of my son and my wife, and I remember thinking about doing the "I love you" transmission and saying goodbye to my wife and my son. I felt so hopeless. I looked back down to see the firefighter below look up at me. At that point, I decided to not do the transmission.

The firefighter below pulled himself up and started yanking on my air pack. I was stuck. He leaned forward and I was able to slide my foot out of my boot. We decided to go out the back way and we jumped off the second-floor balcony to the ground below. I landed on an air conditioner unit, fell again, and lost consciousness. The other firefighter jumped from the second-story balcony and ran over to me. He thought I was dead. Building pieces were falling on us, so he grabbed me and started dragging me. At about that time I regained consciousness. I remember him saying to me, "Holy shit, you fat fuck! Why do we even feed you? Why did I give you dinner last night?" For perspective, he weighs about 160 pounds, and with my gear on I'm about 375 pounds. He had amazing heart—he kept dragging me and cussing me the entire time. He pulled me about twenty yards. He then helped me walk around to the front.

Can you describe your recovery process, when it started and when some of the symptoms started to kick in, letting you know there were possibly some problems?

We went to the ER right away. I called my wife on the way to the hospital. I was on a lot of pain medicine. This is when the white shirts showed up, promising the world and delivering nothing. The doctors did an evaluation and they decided to discharge me. I got home and began to experience so much guilt. The event started to really weigh on me. You are always judged on what you did wrong, not what you did right. I noticed right away that I could not sleep. I could not lay on my left side. If I laid on my left side, it re-triggered the whole experience. It was right in my face the entire time. I could only sleep when I was absolutely exhausted. Then I would have repeated nightmares. Even my wife, Jill, would say that she could tell from my movements in my sleep what part of the memory I was in. Jill pushed me to get help.

Between my burn schedule and my debridement, and with the limited availability of the staff psychologist, it just wasn't working. My mental state was not getting better. I started looking at other avenues. It was two to three weeks of absolute hell. Guilt, the investigation, feeling isolated, the fallout from the event—all this was weighing on me. I reached out to a friend, knowing that she knew what I was going through. I got your name through several contacts. I vetted you through my friend and she told me to go see you right away.

Tell me about your experience with EMDR. How was your recovery process?

I first met you and you started to help me back to myself. I remember at a later point you said, "There you are." I started out in such a dark place and finally started to emerge into who I am. You explained EMDR and I initially thought it was hocus-pocus bullshit. I remember thinking that I needed real help, but then I realized you were really there to help. You were already very protective of me. We did our first session. Up until that point the department had been pushing me to write my report on the incident. I couldn't focus, much less manage writing a report. Just the thought of doing it triggered me to the point that I wanted to crawl out of my skin. I remember doing EMDR the first time and I went home and wrote my entire report. Before EMDR, I couldn't get past the third sentence.

What was it like as your nightmares began to decease and you began to sleep again? When did you start to notice that?

About two weeks after the first EMDR session, there was a slow progression to better and more sleep. After the first session, I finally slept. The nightmares were more like dreams. They were less vivid and intense. The progression just continued. Now I can lay on my left side. There are still events that bring back the memories, but it is no longer right up in my face. That feeling dissipated quickly after EMDR.

How has your recovery experience changed you?

I have always been a the-glass-is-half-full kind of person. I believe going through this has changed me for the better. Going through all this gave me a different lens on life. I see things and people differently than I did before. I relate to people better. I understand people's pain better and can relate to them better.

That's incredible.

It's opened my eyes. You told me trauma causes wisdom, and wisdom causes gray hair. I definitely have more gray hair. I try to make the best out of it.

Tania and Jeremy

Shapiro, Francine. *Eye Movement Desensitization and Reprocessing: Basic Principles, Protocols and Procedures* (New York: Guilford Press, 1995).

Chapter 5
First Responder Suicide

I'm on a downward spiral
Past the breaking point, I've finally hit the wall
A collision course for disaster
Don't give a damn no more, I'm just sick of it all

"Breaking Point" by Digital Summer

Throughout my career, I have found suicide prevention to be one of the most important topics to address in enhancing first responder resilience. I have assisted many departments in the aftermath of suicides and have been asked to consult and train on suicide prevention. Unfortunately, the ripple effects of these awful events are pervasive and run deep. They result in pain, doubt, grief, disbelief, and significant trauma for those who are left behind.

Let's face it—first responders are a population who know how to kill themselves. First responders run calls and see failed suicide attempts every day.

They also see successful suicides. There is no doubt in the mind of a first responder who is spending time on public streets about how one can successfully take one's own life. Our law enforcement community knows that their main mechanism to that end is sitting right there on their hip, day in and day out.

I have noticed two types of causal progressions to suicide by first responders. The first is what I refer to as "psychic battering." Psychic battering is the wear and tear of public safety work that takes a toll over a long time. First responders enter the fields of police, fire, and EMS in part because they are naturally drawn to helping others. However, they soon realize the job also includes significant stress and mental strain. They walk into the worst days of people's lives and see horrific events. Most first responders in the early stages of their careers take cues from the seasoned responders, who will typically demonstrate some type of immunity to such events by either not reacting at all, or by simply using humor as a coping mechanism. While humor is an excellent strategy, just joking about an event will usually diminish or even eliminate the opportunity for crews to truly process the event. The message is that this stuff should not impact you, or if it does, you should brush it off. Meanwhile, field training officers, preceptors, and trainers of young personnel are struggling with the same psychic battering and are suffering internally. They fear that showing their stress will be perceived as weakness, and they are certainly not willing to appear vulnerable to a rookie member of the department. Essentially what happens is that everyone becomes the walking wounded, but no one wants to say anything.

Over time, psychic battering takes a toll on first responders. Seeing tragedy and evil day in and day out can create significant changes in someone's perspective on humanity and life. Psychic battering leads to burnout and anticipatory anxiety about what the next major event might be. It leads to depression, PTSD, and even suicide. The loss of hope, faith, and a healthy perspective all can lead to self-destructive behaviors such as alcohol abuse, dangerous behaviors, and eventually the ultimate act of ending one's life.

One of my former patients who successfully healed was a paramedic who was struggling in all aspects of his life. He was a difficult employee and had been written up several times for his attitude. He essentially told me that he hated his job. His marriage was falling apart and his children were afraid of him. The defining moment that caused him to seek help was when he was standing in the living room of the EMS station and the tones dropped for the first call of the day. He was holding a glass of milk and, as soon as the tones started, he began screaming profanities and threw the glass of milk toward the kitchen sink. The glass hit the cabinet above the sink and the milk, along with glass shards, went everywhere. Welcome to the first call of the day!

I explained the concept of psychic battering to him, and he immediately connected. He agreed this was, in fact, what he was experiencing in his life and career. He reported feeling numb all the time. At this point, I asked him to tell me about the last time he felt something—anything. He looked up and sighed, "Seven years ago on a call. We rolled to a SIDS death and got a pronouncement. At that point, the mother started to scream and I felt a lump in my throat, like I was going to cry. My kid was the same age as the kid we ran the call on. So, I stuffed that feeling down, went numb, and haven't felt anything since." Wow! I am a mostly unflappable therapist, but I was shocked when he said this. I asked if he was ready to change. Of course, he was. Together we did the challenging work of restoring resilience to get his life back. It was hard and demanding work. This client most likely would have committed suicide if he had not received help.

It is imperative that first responders receive help when going through psychic battering. The first and easiest step in addressing psychic battering is to process calls consistently with partners and peers. This simply means hash it out—talk about what happened. Keep talking and keep hashing it out. If a first responder notices that this is not enough, then get in with a good counselor and address the traumas professionally. The most important thing to remember is that the events first responders are exposed to are not normal. Everyone needs help at some point.

The second type of causal progression is what I call "getting stuck in the moment." This is when first responders go through highly traumatic incidents and don't receive sufficient care in the immediate aftermath. As the brain experiences trauma, it becomes wired to "remember," "ruminate," and "focus" on the negative. First responders recall a feeling of helplessness. They focus on the fact that they were not able to do their job. Traumatic events leave dark, negative messages in the minds of first responders. As this perpetuates over the course of the following weeks, they assign some sort of meaning to the event that involves them personally. This forever ties them to the event. They take responsibility for something they did not cause. They blame themselves for not doing more and start to believe they could have done more. In their minds, they become intertwined with the victim or the deceased. The event takes on a life of its own. First responders experience despair, frustration, and an overall lack of ability to move forward.

At our annual training, a peer support team member told me it had been a very rough spring and he had been a "magnet" for every bad pediatric call in the last few months. He explained this was generating a lot of self-doubt and anxiety about future calls. In particular, one call really grabbed his heart and mind. The call was for an unconscious child, unknown cause. When he and his partner arrived, they found a badly beaten boy with various stages of healing injuries. It seems this little five-year-old's life had been one of torture and horrible pain. The final event resulted in extensive brain damage. The child died while enroute to the hospital. The paramedic told me he just could not get past the fact that he unable to do more. He felt helpless. He felt responsible. He felt shame.

I asked him to do three things: First, take a deep breath and take a step back to begin to restore his health through rest and exercise. Incidentally, he had already asked for two shifts off. The second thing I asked him to do was to see this call in a different light. My words to him were, "Here is this tiny, tortured soul. His entire life was pain inflicted by the mother's boyfriend and a mother who failed to protect him. The last person to place hands on this child was you—as a caregiver who was there to finally protect this little guy. His last human contact, as he transitioned away from this world, was not his perpetrator, it was you. And thank goodness you were there for him in his time of need." It was as though a light went on for him. Suddenly the weight of his guilt started to lift. The third thing I asked him to do was to notice normal, happy, healthy children. I encouraged him to go for a run in a park and open his eyes to all the kids playing, joyful and carefree. I asked him to notice vigilant parents standing by to protect their children at any cost. He did. It worked wonders, as his healthy perspective returned by noticing the happy, healthy kids in this world.

What Do We Need to Know About Suicide?

Suicide is almost always linked to a mental health disorder, such as depression, bipolar disorder, or PTSD. Chronic pain is also an issue associated with suicide. Unfortunately, if left untreated, these conditions can become progressively worse. Over time, the brain begins to produce thoughts of suicide as it struggles and fails to overcome the shifts in neurotransmitter levels. The occasional suicidal thoughts initially are typically brushed off, but they become more pervasive and frequent over time. This typically leads to serious consideration and contemplation of suicide.

By the time someone becomes suicidal, they essentially see life through a very narrow tunnel. Their mind truly believes everything and everyone will be better if they take their own lives. They firmly believe there are no options, their situation will never get better, and this is the only and best option. This goes as far as believing those who love them dearly will be relieved when they are gone. This is a very dangerous mindset and belief system. My patients who have been suicidal are shocked when they look back after healing and see how skewed their perspective was. This insight makes them thankful for their lives.

The outward signs we sometimes see when someone is struggling are changes in eating and sleeping patterns, changes in normal day-to-day levels of functioning, and diminished interest in activities. Sometimes first responders will demonstrate behavioral problems at work or risk-taking behaviors that strike their colleagues as too dangerous and inappropriate. Often, we will see a shift from gallows humor to extremely dark humor that is considered over-the-top by others. First responders will speak of suicide on occasion. They will make remarks about taking their lives and how they would do it. Another significant sign is when first responders get their affairs in order and give away their belongings.

Many times there are no signs. Police, fire, and EMS professionals know all too well that if they say anything, someone is likely to act. There are times when personnel take their own lives with no outward warning or indications of struggle. This is absolutely devastating for those left behind. Colleagues experience trauma, grief, and feelings of betrayal. The shock and devastation lasts for a long time and the damage done to fellow first responders is significant.

So, what do we do?

The first step in suicide prevention is to acknowledge the epidemic and the risks associated with this line of work and to act on it. Leadership **must** put in place mandated suicide and substance abuse awareness training in their policies. It must be relevant and to the point. Departmental resources— including clinicians, peer support, and chaplains— **must** be made readily available. They **must** be readily accessible, affordable, or at no cost, and they **must** be confidential. It is highly recommended that these resources be made freely known to all first responders.

Next, change the stigma in the culture. It is impossible to have a good program if leadership refuses to remove the stigma of asking for help or admitting when someone is struggling. Leadership must refrain from making disparaging remarks about suicide or about first responders who have taken their lives. True leadership embraces its people and the struggles they go through. Opening the door to being healthy and recovering from despair by addressing these topics is not opening a can of worms that cannot be closed. If such an attitude by leadership is prevalent, chances of a suicide on their watch will increase exponentially.

Any department can create good awareness campaigns and programs for prevention. If leadership is at a loss on how to proceed, I recommend they hold departmental meetings to listen to feedback from every level, every division, and every age.

Finally, it is important to understand that personnel, given the right avenues to help, can—and do—recover. Admission into an inpatient facility is the highest level of care for someone who is suicidal, which most public safety professionals consider the kiss of death for their careers. This simply is not true, as many first responders have come out of these programs strong and healthy. The key is that leadership understands and embraces the fact that first responders have done the work to heal properly.

The worst-case scenario is that no one does anything. Many years ago, there was a local police officer who worked for a department that was not my customer. On three occasions, he played Russian roulette in the parking lot of his substation in front of his entire shift. No one said or did anything. One day he pulled the trigger and, as fate would have it, the one bullet that was in his revolver impacted his head. It was a horrible, traumatic, tragic day for his entire shift. Afterwards, many of his fellow officers shared with me that they had thought about confronting him—even dragging him into my office—but they never did.

Tania about to hoist up to the Travis County STARFlight helicopter

Tania backstage with Bret Michaels, accepting a donation for veterans with PTSD

Border Patrol Agents showing off their wristbands

Brief after a trauma

Climbing the 75-foot quint at Leander Fire Department

Climbing the 75-foot quint at Leander Fire Department

Flight nurse who has returned to flight

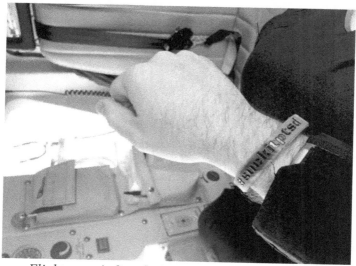

*Flight nurse's first flight after a crash-sporting his
#suckitptsd wristband*

Mike and Tania at the HARTH Foundation (equine therapy)

Tania preparing for live burn at Fire School

Sgt. Chris Kelley Memorial 5K Balloon Release

Sgt. Chris Kelley Memorial 5K Balloon Release

The wristband that Tania placed at the crime scene at the Dallas PD shootings

Tyra the TGA therapy dog

Veterans showing off their wristbands

Tania with Mike Durant, who wrote the foreword

Tania with her mom at a fundraiser for veterans for PTSD treatment

Tania with Vince, aka Rocco Vargas, from Article 15

Responding to active shooter at Fort Lauderdale
International Airport

Mike and Tania at the Police Lives Matter Rally in Austin

Lecturing at a conference

TGA #suckitptsd wrist bands

Chapter 6
Resilience

I don't know what they're talking about
I'm making my own decisions
This thing that I found ain't gonna bring me down
I'm like a junkie without an addiction

"I Don't Wanna Stop" by Ozzy Osbourne

The concept of resilience in today's culture has become an important part of our public safety. Many in leadership positions are embracing the fact that resilient employees make excellent employees. While a resilience initiative is an incredibly important step in the right direction, embracing it is just the first step. The question then is: "How do we create resilience?" This is step two in the process, which is extremely important and where the real preparative work begins.

Many people believe resilience means someone is not impacted by stress. Immunity to stress is actually a form of resistance to stress. Resistance is an important concept all public safety personnel develop over time and with training. It is normal to look back after a year or two—or five or ten—and realize how immune you have become to stress. The initial rough calls that got to you simply don't anymore after experience and time. Our threshold for stress increases over time, based on good training and successful experience. Resistance to stress keeps first responders on the line. Becoming desensitized is a salvation for the human psyche after exposure to stress and trauma.

Resilience refers to the ability of an individual to bounce back during and after adversity. We all experience pain, loss, and trauma that are beyond our coping capacity. Our resilience is our capacity to work through and overcome these challenges. We are all resilient to some degree, but no one is perfectly, completely resilient. Resilience means we are living, working, playing, and loving well. It means we are living the best life possible.

There are some recent studies regarding the resilient brain. As mentioned in Chapter Four, the hippocampus is extremely resilient, as it generates new neural pathways to heal post-trauma. Tapping into the brain's resilience is an exciting new direction to help individuals overcome adversity quickly, and there is much research being done in this area.

One recent study, by the University of Wisconsin-Madison Professor Dr. Richard Davidson, found a correlation between brain structure and resilience. Specifically, this study found that a strong connection between the prefrontal cortex and the amygdala is associated with high resilience. The study compared Navy SEALS with a group of civilians. Stressful images were presented to both groups. Findings showed that the brains of Navy SEALs were successful at managing emotions by nimbly jumping from an emotional reaction to cognition. It was found that with a strong connection between the prefrontal cortex and the amygdala, the SEALs were able to register a graphic image as just that. They then quickly moved from the initial reaction to cognition and control. This same fact is consistent with first responders. A typical first responder will arrive at the scene of something traumatic or gory and will have an internal reaction along the lines of, "Wow! That's bad!" and then quickly jump to protocol, such as, "OK, let's get some gauze on that and stop the bleeding." This internal reaction and mental dialogue is repeated many times through every first responder's career and, thank goodness, they have this capacity. Without it, surviving their career path would be nearly impossible.

Some people are naturally resilient and always have been. This is why first responders gravitate to-

ward their line of work, while others who are less resilient would never become first responders. While
much of our resilience is encoded in our DNA, there
is a certain amount we have to work on to maintain
high resilience. I ask first responders to consider a resilience continuum, where on one end we have low
resilience and on the other end we have high resilience.

Low	Moderate	High

When first responders come to work with low
resilience, it means that if they have a critical incident
or major event, their resilience will be **extremely** low
when the event is over.

Things that lower resilience include lack of rest,
poor hydration, poor nutrition, working too much, relationship stress, financial stress, excessive alcohol
use or abuse, and poor health. When first responders
report for duty and their resilience is low, it's an un-
fortunate setup for big problems in the event of a tragedy, because these types of events tax the resilience of
those who are exposed. On the other hand, if first responders are rested, hydrated, are eating right, and are
tackling life issues as they arise, they are resilient.
When they report for duty, they are ready for whatever rolls their way and they will bounce back well, de-

spite the adversity of a critical incident or high-acuity trauma.

So, now the work of being resilient begins.

Hydration and nutrition: Eating well takes effort. It is sometimes difficult to eat well or even at all during shift work. The most resilient first responders typically plan ahead and bring along foods they want to eat. They are sure to carve out time to eat. Avoiding fast food as much as possible is a good way to build resilience. Having a healthy, balanced diet at work takes planning. While it's impossible to get it right all the time, first responders know they will perform better and feel better overall when eating well. The key to proper nutrition and changing habits to healthier eating has nothing to do with New Year's resolutions or sudden, drastic changes, such as crash diets. Our bodies are delicate systems that habituate to our actions. Changing a diet means gradually pushing bites of what we should not eat off our plate, while gradually incorporating more of what we should eat. Suddenly depriving ourselves of sugars and fats is only going to cause our brains to obsess about those sugars and fats. Not only does the drastic withdrawal make us obsess about the cupcake, it causes our brains to convince us that we need that cupcake—or five of them!

And when it comes to hydration, the key is to do it. First responders work long shifts, work all night long, and have shift changes at some very early hours. Caffeine plays a major role in most shifts for first responders. It is imperative to stay hydrated, and this can be tricky. My favorite tool is the hydration charts that are frequently placed in bathroom stalls, with various shades of yellow to indicate how well hydrated you are based on the color of your urine. The first time I saw one of these was on a Marine Corps base. It took me a minute to figure out the chart, and my colleague in the next stall and I both exclaimed, "Oh! I get it!" We both apparently were in need of one more canteen! It was a good lesson in hydration and it's an easy way to monitor.

Sleep: Getting enough rest is essential to resilience and to the overall well-being of every individual. In public safety, sleep is frequently the ultimate challenge. I ask first responders how their sleep is and the answer is consistently that they don't get enough or don't get good sleep. The disruption of the natural sleep pattern resulting from working shifts, working nights, and just working too many hours creates significant sleep pattern changes in many first responders. Sleeping at a fire or EMS station or an air medical hangar is rarely quality sleep, so even though some professions allow for crew members to rest, most first responders report they really don't sleep well while on duty. I liken on-duty rest to an engine, where the engine represents rescuers' brains. While first responders are not revving that engine when they are sleeping on duty, the engine isn't off, either. The engine is idling. This translates to the feeling of sleeping with one eye open in fear of missing a call, waking up multiple times through the night, or simply not being able to sleep at all.

The key I have found in my work is to encourage public safety personnel to make it a point to get good rest while off duty. This might mean taking naps on their days off. I encourage first responders to do this, especially on their first day off, and to make sure they build in the time to do so. I encourage public safety personnel to take ninety-minute naps in conjunction with the typical sleep cycle. That way, they hit all the stages. There are several sleep apps that are effective in monitoring sleep patterns. They will gently ring an alarm when a full sleep cycle has been achieved.

Other tools I encourage for first responders are things such as going to bed at the same time on off-duty days, decluttering their rooms, making their bedrooms as dark as possible, and developing a routine for bedtime that signals to the brain it's time to decompress. When first responders toss and turn, I encourage them to get up, keep the lights low, and read their books from paramedic school or the penal and traffic codes from their state. That usually does the trick!

Many first responders utilize melatonin, which naturally is released when we are exposed to the dark and when it is bedtime. Melatonin causes the calm, sleepy feeling that signals us to drift off to sleep. The key to melatonin usage is to get good quality brands from vitamin stores, and for first responders to use it only when they cannot sleep. I discourage the automatic use of melatonin without seeing if sleep will come naturally. The chronic use of melatonin will cause the body to simply stop producing melatonin, because it doesn't have to.

I absolutely encourage strong precautions when it comes to sleeping aids, as many are very habit-forming and will create a situation where first responders cannot sleep without them. Withdrawing from sleeping-aid dependence can be very difficult and painful. If first responders go through horrific trauma and cannot sleep, I encourage them to have a conversation with their medical doctor about sleeping aids that are recommended by their physician. I ask first responders to inquire about how much to take and for how long, and to ensure that there is a good discontinuation plan for the medication.

Exercise: The bottom line when it comes to exercise is that it gives the biggest bang for the buck when it comes to mental health. First responders need to work out, not only for strength and safety, but also to keep their brains fit. Exercise improves mood, creativity, problem solving, and sleep patterns. Exercise fights depression. And I jokingly always add in my lectures, "Look how svelte you all look when you work out." There are numerous studies linking exercise to mental and physical health. When a patient starts therapy with me, I always ask about exercise. And if they aren't doing it, well then, they are about to start!

The key to exercise regimens is to set reasonable goals and phase gently into it. In other words, I ask first responders to pick the activities they enjoy most and to set goals, such as two twenty-minute walks in week one, and three twenty-minute walks in week two. We start with reasonable and, of course, enjoyable exercise. I tell public safety personnel all the time if running hurts your knees, don't run. Instead, do what doesn't cause debilitating and discouraging pain. Walk, row, swim, and use the elliptical machine… whatever peaks your interest. I strongly encourage first responders to have an accountability partner, to get on board with Fitbit competitions between shifts or stations, and to have fun with it. I also discourage overarching goals that are not specific, such as, "I am going to get in shape." This is too vague and a huge setup for failure. These types of statements sound much like New Year's resolutions and, as most of us have experienced, are really a recipe for failure. Tangible goals, and objectives to reach those goals, are key when it comes to exercise.

Moral strength: Resilient people are moral. They live with integrity and meaning that is part of their core sense of being. First responders who possess the morality they desire are happier and possess inner peace. This is a work in progress for many of us, and the key to having the desired morality is to keep working on it. In therapy, we take steps to come to terms with a great many things—both professionally and personally. The first step is to own up to what has been done and to commit to a better course of action. From there, we define the course of action in tangible terms, with strategies and objectives to reach those goals. We set out to make all the amends needed to those we have hurt, which is a huge step. Throughout the process, we maintain a "can do" attitude. I encourage first responders to pick themselves up if they fall and to remain tenacious about getting to the point where they want to be. As we grow psychologically and morally, it is common for first responders to set out on a new path to a better life. The growth is amazing to watch.

Altruism: This is the key factor that draws first responders into the profession. They want to help, heal, rescue, stop the evil, and protect the innocent. First responders do this despite the requirement to run toward danger. These professionals have the biggest hearts I have ever witnessed in life. They are just amazing. Altruistic people are very resilient. They possess an inner ability and a drive to walk into any situation that the average person would run away from.

Happiness: Happiness is a combination of genetics and outside factors. Resilient people are typically optimistic and happy people. They have an internal locus of control, which means they are living the life they choose and, for the most part, feel strongly in control of where their lives are heading. They choose their career paths and families, and they choose to live the lives they want to lead. Understanding they can't and don't control everything, resilient people anticipate that there will be setbacks and issues that come up, but they approach them with an attitude to create change for stabilization of their situation. Resilient people live mostly happy lives based on choices that enhance their resilience. While we can't control the genetics connected to our happiness, we can manage the external factors that improve happiness: exercise, vitamin D, sunlight, engaging in problem solving, and maintaining organization in our lives. The other thing associated with happiness is the ability to keep things in perspective. When we realize the big picture is not necessarily related to how we feel or our perceptions, we remember to keep it all in perspective and in turn stay focused on managing our stress, rather than letting things get to us.

Faith: Whatever their faith, I ask first responders to stay in touch with this aspect of their lives. First responders who have faith possess an inner peace. They typically have a whole family outside of their public safety job that loves them and will stand by them. I have found that first responders who use their faith to help themselves heal will do so rapidly and effectively. Some of the most difficult clients I have had are first responders who have sustained trauma and simultaneously walked away from their faith as a result of the trauma. If there are struggles with faith after a trauma, I am quick to involve members of the clergy whom first responders like and trust. Leadership in faith is extremely important during times of questioning the reasons behind an occurrence. If faith is a component of a first responder's life, I will always ask them to seek guidance and support from that resource as well.

Miranda's Story

Miranda is a flight nurse and a member of the peer support team for one of my national customers. When I first met Miranda, she could not think of one nice thing to say about herself. As I got to know her during training, I started to see a big picture of burnout, fatigue, and despair. Then suddenly it started to turn around. Today Miranda is a resilient, strong, amazing woman who is passing her wisdom onto others who are in need. Her story is amazing.

Tell me your story about your burnout, how it started and how it manifested.

I think I have always been one of those people with a lot of irons in the fire. Jumping into the world of EMS at nineteen years old and climbing the ladder to paramedic, I can honestly say my life revolved around my job. I have heard you say in training that we are not just the job, but I really was the job. My life was being a paramedic. It was the only identity I felt I had and everything revolved around EMS. At a very young age I gave up a lot of things and started living as a very responsible adult, working three jobs.

My big event happened in March 2002. I was working a terrible car accident. Long story short, I elected to do an emergency cricothyrotomy on a trauma patient who had lost his airway. Unfortunately, when we were originally on the way to the hospital, we realized that we had left our equipment in the back of a pickup truck on the scene, so we had no way to re-intubate him and he was in full traumatic arrest. I made a split-second decision to do an emergency cricothyrotomy. Obviously, it didn't work and he died. Had it worked, I probably would have been a hero, but he didn't live.

At the time, I was twenty-five years old and only the second female paramedic in my small rural community in southern Indiana. I learned very quickly that young, ambitious women don't do well in these types of environments. A week later, I got a call from my medical director and hospital administrators. They called me in and suspended me. They sent it to the state EMS Commission. The next thing I knew, I was in the headlines in the newspaper and all this just took off with a life of its own. I had a ten-month suspension and was in the newspaper thirty-six times in my small town, where I was born and raised. It got ugly. People went to the Commissioners' meetings stating things about me personally, nothing related to work. People wrote letters about my personality and sent them to the state EMS Commission, which then forwarded these letters to my attorney. I faced these very people in the grocery store, and they were totally fake. It was a hard lesson to learn at a young age.

The following October, I had a hearing with an administrative law judge. Out of sixteen counts, he found me guilty of one, which was not following airway protocol and not trying a less-invasive airway prior to trying the end-all. This was fine. I had to live with the decision I had made. I just wanted my job back. The judge recommended eighteen months of suspension and remedial training. It went back to the EMS Commission and in January there was a meeting. My attorney and I were told not to come. This meeting was on a Friday, and the following Monday morning the headlines in the paper read, "Local Paramedic Certification Revoked for Seven Years." They took it all. They didn't even listen to the judge. They took everything—all my certifications. In an instant, my identity was gone.

I didn't know what to do. I wallowed in my apartment for about a week until a couple friends dragged me out and said that they were not going to let this destroy me. In the meantime, I had a knee injury and I was recovering from surgery. I was completely overwhelmed.

I don't know how or where I began, but I decided I had to start over. I needed a job, so I took one as a federal security guard. I carried a 9mm and an M-16 for a year and a half. I got myself back into school and decided to go to nursing school. I called the state board of nursing and asked if I could become a nurse after the loss of my paramedic licensure. They told me they did not know, but I knew I belonged in health care, so I took the leap of faith and started school. I went back to work in the hospital where I had attended paramedic school. I worked weekends and went to school during the week.

I told my nursing instructors and my classes what happened. I owned it. I didn't hide from it. I bawled like a baby every time I told the story. When I became a nurse, there was a lot of pressure not to mess up. I began to prove everyone wrong. I moved to a big city and became an ER nurse. I became a charge nurse. That was where I was born as a nurse. I began to gain as much experience as I could to become a flight nurse. I worked very hard.

In the meantime, I started a humane society. I became active in so many avenues. I soon realized that I had created a monster. I was a public figure who had to be perfect all the time and who had to work all the time. I never said no. This lasted for six years. Every year I hit burnout. Every fall I struggled with burnout and once got called out for it in the hospital.

I had no idea why I was the way I was until I met you. I started to understand myself. I realized that

I have a Type A personality and that I needed to change my life. I had a very hard time figuring out how to do this and I would make small changes, only to go back to the way I had been. One day I was driving home after a rough week and I lost my shit on the side of the road. I pulled over, vomited, was shaking, crying, and having palpitations. I felt like I was having a heart attack. I realized at that moment that I needed to change my life.

I started to try to achieve balance. I began to change my eating habits and my lifestyle. I resigned from the humane society, which was huge. Two months later, I filed for divorce. I had been in a bad marriage for a long time. I moved and started to re-build. Slowly but surely, over a year, I gave up all my part-time jobs. I focused on me, my one job, my life, my health, and my fitness. For the first time ever, I made myself a priority. This year I decided to take it to the next level. I have lost a ton of weight and am an avid cross-fitter. The community at cross-fit is amazing. They are a whole new outlet for support.

I finally feel like I have balance and I have nothing left to prove to anyone. I can live my life every day. It's amazing to say, because to come from where I was to where I am now… I am still the same person, but life is *so* grand. I wake up every day excited about the people in my life, the things that are happening in my life. I am not tired, I am not exhausted mentally, physically, and emotionally like I used to be. It's just a whole different world. I see burnout in my colleagues. Part of surviving burnout has been to travel across the country and do my burnout lecture. If I can touch people in a positive way and have an impact, it is all worth it. I don't want anyone to go through what I have been through. I realize through meeting you that, while I thought my goal was to become a flight nurse, I now realize my future goal is to turn around and help people in public service. We are a special breed, and I don't want public safety personnel to suffer like I did. We must take care of our own. I am going to pay it forward.

Miranda and Tania

Chapter 7
Clinicians: Know Your Audience

We ain't super heroes, we're just ordinary people
Trying to make a difference and the first on scene
It's a heavy, heavy burden, to carry all this hurtin'
When you can't unsee the things you see
It keeps going on when those sirens are gone

"When Those Sirens Are Gone" by Ken Davison and Doug
Folkins

The key to providing good care is excellent customer
service and the ability to reach out and touch the lives
of first responders, and to know who they truly are.

Anyone who wants to work with first responders
must do their homework up front: get to know the
amazing people who carry so much responsibility on
their shoulders. Their careers represent so much more
than just jobs, or what they do for a living. To be effective, they must develop significantly difficult skill
sets and very distinct cultures, lifestyles, and mentali-
ties. They have weird schedules, speak in very distinct

nomenclatures, and form close-knit, super-tight associations and affinities with their teams.

One of the best things clinicians can do is to go on ride-alongs with public safety personnel. It involves many hours of hopping into patrol cars, ambulances, and fire trucks. You are exposed to an amazing wealth of experiences. You start to understand the mindset of first responders when you see them in action. If you are lucky, they will get you involved in some of the things happening. I strongly believe it is imperative in order to build rapport, credibility, and trust. With time, you learn to focus on the radio and understand codes and abbreviations that are so prevalent in their world, and you also begin to understand the intricate elements of each culture.

Riding along with a law enforcement officer teaches the importance of safety, situational awareness, and teamwork. The eye-opening realities of enforcing our laws, the self-control that officers must maintain in extremely high-stress situations, and the actual copious report writing—these are all things no one really understands until they experience it on that level. Police officers have very distinct dialogues that encompass ten-codes and pretty much the most blatant, realistic, and blunt assessments of any situation. You must know and understand all this to be effective.

Further, riding along teaches you to experience totally chaotic situations that cause a full adrenaline rush, followed by hours of quiet and sheer boredom, and the delicate balance of managing a post-adrenaline dump that can mean absolute exhaustion on a long shift.

Going Code 3 toward shots fired can be one of the most amazing experiences ever. I challenge my readers who may be critical of how law enforcement do their job: go ahead, see if you can handle it.

One of my most memorable ride-alongs with law enforcement was with the Austin Police Department. I have ridden with the APD many times, but this one was quite remarkable. Overall, the shift was fairly normal, with the usual run of Friday night calls involving intoxication and violence. Just another Friday night in the city. Around 1:30 a.m., the officer I was riding with found a driver's license. We made our way to the owner's house. As we approached, we heard a loud boom, the distinct sound of a high-speed collision. No words necessary, we ran back to the patrol car to hurry toward the source of the loud boom.

The officer notified dispatch of the direction we were heading, 911 calls started to come in, and it was clear there was a high-speed collision involving two vehicles on US Highway 290 eastbound. My escorting officer and I were first on scene and it was unbelievable. A woman had run out of gas and stopped on the side of the highway. Two gentlemen came to her rescue and were pushing her car to a gas station about half a mile away. The owner of the vehicle was in the driver's seat, steering her car in neutral. Unfortunately, a drunk driver was heading eastbound on Highway 290 and, as intoxicated drivers do, he veered toward the lights of the woman's vehicle without realizing it. He impacted her, going approximately eighty miles an hour.

I was an EMT at the time, so I told the officer I was going to try to help the victims. He began to direct traffic and secure the scene, and EMS arrived shortly thereafter. What I found was one of the gentlemen, who had landed in a ditch. He was obviously dead on the scene (DOS). As I ran down Highway 290, I found the other gentlemen's foot and about half his calf. I came upon him just as EMS arrived. He was found viable at the time, but later died at the hospital. Once this gentleman was loaded on Travis County's STAR*Flight*, I went to the woman and tried to console her. As could be expected, she was extremely distraught and was transported to the hospital for emotional care.

I then tried to find my APD ride-along officer in the chaos. I saw him pull back up to the scene in his patrol car. Turns out, during the time I was trying to help the victims, the officer found the license plate of the assailant's vehicle. He "ran the plate," got an address, took off, arrested the suspect, brought him back, picked me up, and we transported him to jail. Adrenalin was through the roof. We laughed all the way to the jail because of incredible timing and unbelievable speed of action within a multi-faceted chaos. It felt like a television show, where the crime is solved in an hour!

Riding out with Emergency Medical Services is also a very distinct experience that shows the amazing skills and talents of professional care providers under extremely stressful situations. Unbelievable is the medical care they provide to patients in the back of ambulances, or in a crashed vehicle, in a ditch, or in a tree. Paramedics joke that they cannot really start IVs while standing in a quiet room. Instead, they say they can "nail" any IV in total chaos, with loud yelling and being bounced around in an ambulance that is racing to the hospital.

Emergency Medical Services folks essentially bring a mobile emergency room to the place of need. Here they see some of the most critically injured and ill patients in medicine. They see people on the worst days of their lives and manage their illnesses and injuries with skill and compassion at a tempo that is mind-boggling. They continue these missions in all types of weather and the challenges of surrounding situations. At the same time, they offer support and calm to family members of the injured and ill.

Emergency Medical Services folks work incredible shifts. Back-to-back calls frequently result in hours of hard work and heavy lifting, with no chance to stop for food or take time to actually pee. Forget taking a break! Then consider the extreme mindset and emotional shifts that EMTs and paramedics must make as they balance the very critical calls with the numerous, relentless calls from the patients who are considered "frequent flyers," as they call 911 repeatedly for toe pain, headaches, heartaches, and boredom. EMS people are amazing.

The most distinct EMS ride-along I like to share is one involving a very busy shift, full of gunshot wounds, stabbings, motor vehicle accidents, and assaults. I was riding with a downtown crew from the Austin Travis County EMS, and we had settled into a good groove of taking calls and helping patients. We took a call (I honestly cannot remember what the call was for) and, while enroute, we heard a loud bang. We started wondering if we had blown a tire or if the engine was about to catch on fire, but all the instrument lights remained normal. We picked up our patient and took him to the hospital. While on the ER dock, one of the paramedics discovered the source of the bang: a slug in the side of the ambulance. Someone had shot the ambulance while we were heading toward our call. We stared at the slug in disbelief. Two paramedics kept saying, "But we're here to help, we're the good guys." It makes me sad to think how much our society has changed and the fact that even helpers and the good guys have become targets of hate.

Riding along with firefighters is another unique experience that lends itself to tremendous insight into what it takes to fight fires, and to do it safely. The mechanics of firefighting requires a great deal of skill and incredible bravery. The risks firefighters must take are at times unbelievable, and they do it willingly. The firefighter culture is also unique. Firefighters break bread together as family and laugh, argue, get mad, and smooth things out much like families with multiple siblings. They love to play pranks on one another. Thick skin is a must in their culture.

My favorite ride-along with a fire department was very entertaining, as it was an unexpected ride-along. I was doing a trauma and stress management class for a group of volunteer firefighters just north of San Antonio. About halfway through my class, the "tones" went off, indicating they had a call, a structure fire, and, of course, they all had to leave the class. I was joking about how I had never cleared a room of firefighters thus far in my career when one of them ran by, grabbed me, and yelled, "Come with us." He didn't have to ask me twice! I jumped on the engine and took a seat where I was told. Somehow, on the way to the call, extra bunker gear and an extra helmet appeared, so I put that on over my professional clothes, which was quite the sight apparently, because they were cracking up the whole time. Someone tossed out the nickname "Firefighter Barbie" and it stuck. We spent the afternoon at the structure fire and somehow, in the midst of all this, I was able to finish my class. I had so much fun that day. Although, I did admit to them that I had no idea what I was doing and wished I could help more. They assured me I was doing plenty. Two weeks later a package arrived at my office—it was a Barbie doll decked out in tiny bunker gear that apparently came off some other type of doll. The note read, "Thanks for the great class, and for helping us with the fire."

One of the most amazing experiences that takes good timing, strong connections, and a stroke of luck is to fly along with air medical or airborne law enforcement. Safety is an absolute must and always takes top priority. Watching and learning from flight crews is one of the most enriching ride-alongs you can have. These professionals are at the top of their game, are stellar performers, and are some of the hardest-charging people I have met. They start their careers as patrol officers, ER or ICU nurses, and street medics. They rise to the top of their game and are recruited and selected based on skills, commitment, personalities, and just having "the right stuff." Their normal duties include everything they typically do, in addition to the complications of flight. The aircraft is a completely different vessel, and it takes hundreds of hours to become truly proficient at performing their duties in the air.

One of my "fly-alongs" involved a motorcycle accident with two victims. The driver was intoxicated, driving way too fast. The passenger was his girlfriend and when she flew off the motorcycle, she was going at such a rate of speed that she actually bent a post of encased electrical wires on impact at the side of the highway. She was pronounced dead on the scene, but her boyfriend apparently was going to be fine in the long run. We flew him to the trauma center, and while enroute to the hospital, he repeatedly attempted to assault the flight nurse. At one point the nurse got into this guy's face and threatened to toss him out of the helicopter. Enough said. He stopped fighting.

Ride-alongs are a must. They bring insight, understanding, and appreciation for the actual work done by professionals. Ride-alongs give clinicians credibility. When you show up, you learn, spend time with, and experience things at a whole different level. The more you ride, the more emergency services personnel have the opportunity to get to know and trust you. If some day they do come in for help, they don't have to explain their terminology, because you already know it. Speaking the language means fewer barriers.

Another important aspect of riding along is learning about the specific culture of the group you are working with. The United States Border Patrol and the New York Police Department are both law enforcement agencies. But their roles, functions, terminology, and duties—in short, their worlds—are vastly different. Understanding their cultures is imperative.

Our military is also very, very important. Spending time with military members and attending as many events for veterans as you can is a great way to understand their cultures. None of us should assume we can treat military members unless we have spent time with those who serve. Do spend time to familiarize yourself with military terms. Ask them about the rank structure. Ask about the differences between the branches. Read books written by our veterans. Spend time at military appreciation events and volunteer for organizations that help our military members.

One of the highlights of my career has been my work with the Marine Corps. I spent several years doing pre- and post-deployment briefs for the Marine Air Group 41 (MAG-41) and the 4th Marine Division. The United States Marine Corps is one of the most distinct, amazing, and awesome cultures I have ever been around. They are also blunt, rough, and hard-core. Before I ever did briefs for groups of Marines, the colonel, who facilitated my introductions to the Marine Corps, put me in front of Marines who were selected to help me out—to break me in, really. Not only did I get a crash course in terminology, I was also trained how to talk like a Marine. I will never forget this group of hard-charging, knuckle-dragging, mean-as-hell Marines telling me, "Don't use that word ever again. It's stupid. Marines won't like it. What the hell, anyway? How do people come up with words like that?" They were referring to my use of the word "affect"; when I'd first used it, they'd asked what I meant, and when I explained that it meant emotion, they threw stuff! I grew very close to this group of warriors and am eternally grateful for their assistance. I was fully broken in by the time the war in Iraq went to all-out intensity, and I was ready for anything that landed in front of me during a brief or in my office. *Semper Fidelis.*

Chapter 8
Public Safety Therapy

I think I need help
Cause I'm drowning in myself
It's sinking in, I can't pretend
That I ain't been through hell

"Help" by Papa Roach

For the first few years of my career, I worked in a Level II trauma center and the majority of my time there was on Friday, Saturday, and Sunday night shifts. I was building my practice slowly during the week, and on Thursday night it was time to switch my sleep patterns back to the night shift rhythm. I made the choice each Thursday to ride along with police, fire, and EMS. Not only were these some of the best experiences to help me understand the population I would ultimately serve, it also gave me exposure and credibility. It was no accident that my practice quickly began to reflect a high percentage of emergency services professionals. These folks are intelligent and quick to judge, they are intuitive and perceptive, and they have hugely strong "bullshit meters." They can sniff out your weakness, fear, and uncertainty. Once they do, the relationship between you and your client is over. My relationships with my clients are based on customer service. Respect, trust, skill, and credibility are the crux of the relationship. Of course, not all my clients have been happy with therapy when they realize it is never my job to placate or enable bad behaviors. The importance of direct, clear, and effective intervention is the foundation of helping first responders find their paths to healing, to getting better.

The first step is to get first responders through the door. By the time they reach out for help, the vast majority of my clients state they have been thinking about calling me for a year. They initiate emails requesting help by saying they have started that email a hundred times. They disclose that they picked up the phone many, many times before they actually made the call. Requesting help from a mental health professional is, to many first responders, the ultimate act of weakness or admission that they have lost control. The negative connotations of asking for help are very threatening and intimidating to them. First responders are worried they will lose control if they ask for help. They worry they will be judged, they won't be understood, or worse, they will be diagnosed with something that is career-ending. It is especially pervasive in the field of law enforcement because many officers consider a mental health diagnosis the 'kiss of career death." Anything that threatens productivity, money, or a career is obviously very hard to consider, and this is why most first responders either wait to make the call for help or just simply suffer.

A rescuer's first call for help is paramount. I check my voicemail and email multiple times a day. I call potential clients back as quickly as possible, and I expect the same of my clinical team. I make my mobile number readily available to all of my customers, and on my business card. During that first call, I reassure first responders it is OK to ask for help, and I promise to take good care of them. I schedule them as quickly as possible to reduce anxiety and to assure the likelihood they will follow through with the appointment. I also explain how the billing works with the contracts I have (see Chapter One), to reassure new clients their identity will not be disclosed to their department, and I reassure them there is no paper trail that can link information to the fact they are getting care.

The first appointment is a critical phase for first responder therapy. I try to schedule a first responder's initial appointment with no one in the hour before their session as much as possible. If they arrive early, I take them back to my office as quickly as possible, thereby eliminating wait time. It is intimidating to sit in a waiting room and think about the reasons one has made this type of appointment. If there is a time for fear and self-doubt to kick in, it is during that time. I essentially do my best to bring them straight from the front door right into my counseling room.

During a first session, it is imperative that first responders are put at ease. Reiterating confidentiality and safety are paramount. First responders need to be heard and they need to know they can address their issues confidently at their own pace. Since the mantra for most public safety personnel is "fix me yesterday," it is vital that goals are set early on. My style is very direct, but also laid back. First responders bring a tremendous amount of anxiety and energy to therapy; therefore, I tend to simply roll with them while communicating very clearly. As the problems are identified, public safety folks need a plan and a path ahead. If they see a therapist who spends three sessions gathering history, they will likely quit therapy. By the end of the first session, it is important to have goals and objectives to reach those goals. I don't call this a treatment plan. In my office, it's called the "plan of attack."

After the initial session, first responders need a sense of how long they will spend in therapy. Expect them to want to move quickly. They typically do not desire or intend to spend months in therapy. They want to feel progress each week as they move toward resolution of their issues. First responders want feedback and they want homework. They typically do their homework readily and will expect each subsequent week to build on the previous one. They are used to training that is sequential, with skill building and progression in competence. They want the same form of therapy. Clinicians need to keep it moving forward.

An important part of establishing goals and a path forward is the very important relationship between first responders and the therapist. First responders are skeptical of mental health professionals. They think of therapists as "touchy feely" and weak. When they walk through that door, they need to understand on some level that the therapist has their back and is committed to helping. If they detect the therapist is intimidated, shocked, or horrified at their work stories, or even aloof, they will quit therapy. It is quite normal for a first responder to ask their therapist questions not just about their experience, but about the therapist's life. If you are a therapist and you want to work with first responders, you better be ready to answer those questions. If graduate school taught you to never answer questions about your life, then you are not a good fit for first responders. They exist in a world of partnerships and, as partners, they know each other extremely well. They also exist in a world where they ask perfect strangers many personal questions in order to perform their job. They will not attend sessions and self-disclose if they feel it is a one-way street. Therapists who see rescuers need to keep it real and be human beings. In other words, a therapist cannot hide behind a façade of perfectionism and make progress with the client.

Understanding public safety terminology is important to the therapeutic relationship. Having to explain what it means to intubate a patient or being in pursuit is frustrating for first responders. If they have to explain to the therapist what their job duties are, it will be perceived as a waste of time. When public safety personnel start talking, they want to be heard. The flip side is that therapists need to use caution with the mental health terminology they use. First responders do not like to talk about feelings. In my office, I joke that the "f word" is feelings. We don't use that word. (We use the other "f word" a lot, though!) First responders tend to swear a lot. Clinicians should be really comfortable with this. Therapists also need to be cautious of using what first responders refer to as

psychobabble. Pervasive use of psychological terminology will turn them off. Therapists should remember that no first responder wants to be diagnosed with
anything that is career-threatening or career-ending,
so caution must be used when explaining diagnoses.
Since I am on contract with my customers, I do not
bill insurance and hence there is no paper trail to link
a diagnosis to my patients. This method should be
considered by all departments (see Chapter One on
having a plan). And, most certainly, this increases the
likelihood that first responders will get help.

Another very important aspect of therapy with
first responders is that therapists had better understand
what they are getting into when it comes to treating
trauma. I can't count the number of times first responders have told me they went to a session and the
therapist was horrified when the first responder described a "normal shift." Never mind the fact that the
client went to a really terrible incident, but was never
able to address it because the therapist was crying by
the end of the session. This is an absolute failure on
the part of the therapist. If a therapist wants to work
successfully with first responders, they need to go on
ride-alongs to really know what such a shift is all
about. First responders come to therapy with what I
call "furnace-blast trauma." It's bad. It's gory. It's
scary. Therapists who advertise they work with trau-

ma frequently are looking for patients who perhaps went through some childhood trauma and who have mostly resolved these traumas. This is not public safety trauma. First responders may have walked into the worst day of someone's life, and in turn this sometimes becomes the worst day of their career.

When police officers are directed to a therapist after a shooting, it is absolutely vital that the clinician is very familiar with law enforcement. Understanding the use-of-force continuum, decision-making during high-stress situations, physical and psychological reactions after a strong fight-or-flight response, as well as the aftermath of a shooting that includes departmental policies, stress of the investigation, disruption of an officer's schedule, media and community reaction, and the impact on the officer's family: all these consequences are essential prerequisites of knowledge for the clinician. Police officers are at a crossroads after a shooting and the paths they can go down are either one of increased resilience as they return to duty after a shooting, or the alternative. I have seen shootings ruin careers, lives, and families. PTSD, isolation, anger, fear of reprisal, and financial ruin from the disruption of overtime are all factors that can negatively impact law enforcement officers after a shooting. One of my former clients told me about a shooting he was involved in when employed by another agency. I asked him about his care after the shooting. He frowned and responded, "Well, the therapist asked me how I felt about my shooting, and I told her I felt pretty good about it. It was, after all, completely justified. She looked at me and proceeded to tell me that I should feel horrible because I killed someone. I never went back. I wonder how she would feel if someone pointed a gun at her." This is an epic failure and is unacceptable.

Trust is the most important aspect of any therapeutic relationship. First responders need to have trust in their therapist and in the process. They expect clinicians to keep it real, to roll up their own sleeves with the patient, and attack the traumas as a team. They need clinicians who are direct, transparent, and who really care. They do not tolerate fake, aloof, vague, or sterile responses.

Availability between sessions is another important part of the therapeutic process. My patients know they can reach me any time they are in crisis. They have my mobile number. They understand I don't want them to text me at 11:00 p.m. to reschedule a session the following week, but they know that if something happens and they need me, I am there for them. To me, it's about customer service and teamwork. When patients feel that dedication and connection, they build trust, take therapeutic risks, and heal.

One thing therapists need to remember, also, is that many public safety personnel who come to therapy have not been taking care of themselves personally. One of the first steps in therapy is to send first responders to their medical doctors for check-ups and evaluations of overall health, including blood tests. Adrenal fatigue, low testosterone, thyroid issues, and high cortisol levels are frequently found in first responders due to the nature of the job—multitudes of fight-or-flight reactions occur on a frequent basis. Many of these issues, when addressed by physicians, will alleviate some of the mental health issues that first responders present to the therapist.

Denise's Story

Denise is a detective with a Central Texas police department. She was one of my hardest patients to treat, given the severity of her trauma and the many facets of her life that were constantly triggering her consistently and severely. We worked very hard together as a team. Today, she is doing incredibly well. I joke that Denise caused me a ton of gray hair, but there is total truth in this.

All right, Denise, talk to me.

When we first met, it was like I was not myself. It was like an out-of-body experience. I never felt right. We had this order saying we had to go to annual training and there was this section saying we had to go to a training by this lady on post-traumatic stress disorder. I was like, "Why?" It's offensive being in law enforcement and having to go to this type of training. But then, the night before I met you, it was so bad that I was in my closet with a loaded gun in my face and I was going to kill myself. I look back now, after working with you, and realize it wasn't so much that I wanted to die, I just wanted it to stop. Just for a second. I didn't have the tools to make things slow down.

I went to your class and you were talking to all the officers and you were describing me. The symptoms of PTSD, the things that happen in your mind, the chemicals that fire in your brain... you were describing me. I was so irritated that I got up and left your class, but then you kept talking, so I came back. Things started making sense. Then you said something along the lines of a person with PTSD being explosive and having no filter. The whole class turned around and looked at me, and I made a joke of it, but something in me knew I needed help.

I started thinking about what I'd experienced the night before in my closet, and I sent you the first text message. I knew you could help me. It took a lot of courage for me to send the message. When you described PTSD, it's like it went from a stigma to being the real deal with these chemicals firing in your brain, and it made sense. I have been through a lot and when Bobby died, everything snapped. I had been basically white-knuckling it since July, when Bobby, a fellow officer who I helped train, died, until February, when I met you. My life was out of control.

After talking to you, I have tools now to take a breath and have learned that being a police officer is who I am, but having PTSD is not who I am.

What was it like the first time you came to a session with me? The very first time?

Oh, it was scary. I was terrified. You were really cool, you didn't flaunt your degrees on the wall or anything. When I talked to you, it was like you knew the police really well. It's like you have a cop brain. And you understood, you took everything that was all twisted up in me and broke it down, one thing at a time. Instead of talking about twelve things at once, you made it manageable chaos.

How long did it take for you to start to trust?

Oh, dear God. A long while. I mean, I trusted you with something every time I came to talk to you, but it took a while. I mean, a long while.

Do you remember what made you start to trust?

Yeah—when I would be sarcastic and you would look at me like, "OK, that's funny." And you would laugh. I mean, you were a human being. You got my humor. I think the breakthrough was one day when I came in and I was having a meltdown. I kept saying, "Can I leave now?" And I totally had the freedom to get up and walk out, but I look back on that day and realize I was waiting for you to say, "Yeah, you can go" so I could turn around and say, "See, it doesn't work." But you kept me talking and I was just rambling and after I got done with all this rambling, you looked at me and asked, "Do you want some water?" and that was the day I started to trust you. You were always Tania, the doctor, but it was like you were Tania, the friend. And you never wrote shit down in front of me. How can any shrink do that to a cop? I mean, I know you keep notes, but I totally felt like you were paying attention when you never wrote stuff down in front of me. You just paid attention and took things one step at a time.

We texted a lot between sessions. How helpful was that?

That was great, because after I talked to you for a while, I realized I could text you about any issue and you would remind me to breathe and take things one step at a time. It always made sense. The best advice you ever gave me was in a text, when you told me to get some sleep. You taught me to slow it all down.

How has conquering PTSD helped your career?

Oh my God. I was on a path to so much trouble. Since treatment, I have received awards. My partner is my best friend. Everything is calm and I can write my reports. I can take things in order. It has made my life so much better. I don't drink anymore, at all. I used to drink all the time and I used to drink to fall asleep. I am going to the gym and seeing results. I quit smoking and I feel great. I manage my life so much better. I used to do such dumb shit. Not anymore.

I don't work in a place that supports officers. They don't care if their officers get help. There are a lot of departments like that. That means I had to get help on my own. And it was totally worth it. If you don't get help, you'll do something stupid. You'll end up in prison or hurting someone. You'll end up killing yourself. If you think you can handle it yourself, you're wrong.

Going back to the therapy process, during our time together, do you think there was a time when you were testing me?

Oh, yes.

It was almost like you were making sure I would not fail you. What could I have done that would have failed you? What would have made you walk out and never come back?

If what we talked about—if I had heard that outside of your office—I would have quit. Or maybe if you had told me that my PTSD was less important than, say, an officer who was involved in a shooting. That would have made me quit. If I ever heard what I shared with you outside of your office, I would have set your house on fire.

I believe it!! Did you ever feel judged?

No. Not with you. Never. No matter what I said, you rolled with it. Especially my humor. You gave me tools every time I talked with you. It clicked. It worked. You never acted like a shrink.

Tania and Denise

Chapter 9
Peer Support

Hit the pit
Blood on the bricks
Don't look back 'cause I got your six
Won't go down, never gonna quit
Don't look back 'cause I got your six

"Got Your Six" by Five Finger Death Punch

The concept of peer support has emerged extensively in the past twenty years. In my opinion, it has been an absolute blessing to public safety. Applied correctly, peer support is one of the biggest assets any organization can have. Through my customers, I train and work with amazing peer support teams. As a clinician, I consider peer support teams an extension of my practice. I absolutely love working with the teams and really could not do my work well without them. If you are a clinician who wants to work in public safety but does not believe in peer support, you may as well consider whether or not you want to work with first responders at all.

Peer support consists of recruiting and training the right personnel, and guiding them as they, in turn, support their colleagues. Some teams cover only their own agency, while others cover multiple agencies in a collaborative spirit. My model for teaching peer support is based on the needs of each particular agency and their specific area of need. The bottom line is to have peers in place who can objectively and quickly respond to fellow first responders when an incident happens.

One of the first steps in establishing a peer support team is to obtain complete buy-in from leadership and a well-written set of standard operating procedures (SOPs). While there are many good formats that can be used and shared, it is nonetheless important to adjust the SOPs to reflect the needs and goals of the agency or agencies involved. Having standard operating procedures available prior to initial training is very helpful, because students will have an opportunity to ask questions about protocol and expectations during the first day of training.

Members of a peer support team should be chosen based on their merits. Every team should consist of public safety personnel who are good performers, who do not have ongoing personal issues or complaints against them, and who are natural leaders that other first responders gravitate toward for guidance or support. The best peer support team members are naturally easy-going and are passionate about looking out for their colleagues. They are trustworthy, and while they possess the gift of gab, they are also good at being tight-lipped. However, I have noticed in my peer support training that leadership will sometimes send one or two students who "need to be fixed" in hopes that the class will assist them with whatever their struggles are. I explain to leadership that training for a peer support team is not the proper avenue to fix those problematic employees. In fact, I need the most resilient employees to build an effective team.

Team members are usually chosen through an application process with a letter of recommendation from a supervisor and a peer colleague. Once the applications are in, I prefer to interview the candidates myself so I can get a sense of their commitment and ability to respond, based on the particular needs of the team. It gives me time to explain what the process is all about and allows me to answer any questions the candidate might have.

Once team members are chosen, it is time to proceed with their training. The training can be anywhere from three days to two weeks, depending on the needs of the organization. Obviously, the more time we have, the better they'll be prepared. Although the content of their training can vary, it must include the following points at a minimum, in my opinion:

1. In-depth training on fight or flight, stress, and trauma
2. Stress management and self-care
3. Confidentiality
4. Triaging during and after a crisis
5. Interventions—how to do each one and in-depth discussions of how to do them correctly
6. Communication training—listening and dialogue
7. Problem solving without fixing
8. Extreme crises and suicide
9. Limits of peer support
10. Standard operating procedures
11. Outside resources and when to refer
12. Statistics-keeping and team expectations

Training should consist of time to practice and implement the concepts learned. Putting it into action is an essential part of training, as peer support team members must be coached out of their comfort zones. First responders are required to take control of people and solve their problems on a daily basis. This is their job. During training, I teach first responders how to stop "fixing" when they are in this role, and instead serve as a resource and catalyst for change. It takes time to adjust to this kind of mindset, so practice and feedback are imperative.

The best class is a fun class. Adult learners need variety and they need to be engaged. I tell my students that I teach like "romper room." We typically lecture and hit the heavy topics in the morning. In the afternoons, when students are tired, we switch to videos, discussions, and practice. My classes are a bit like roller-coasters—we address some very hard topics and I use equally difficult experiences from my career to illustrate how responses work. And then I pull my audience from difficult experiences to something lighthearted. We laugh a lot in class and sometimes we cry. The key is to make it the most meaningful class they will ever have, because at the end of it they will go out and save fellow rescuers' lives.

One of the key components of peer support is confidentiality. Each state is different when it comes to confidentiality. There are federal mandates stating that peer support is confidential. Many states have deemed peer support as confidential in health and safety codes. If this is not the case in your state, it must become step one in your training, because peer support must be confidential.

Limits to confidentiality are clear and understandable: Peer support cannot keep in confidence any threat to harm self or others, child or elder abuse, or criminal activity that could impact a colleague's employment. I train my teams to know this and to adhere to it. Peer support team members must explain this fact to any peer who asks to speak to them in this capacity. I never allow team members to simply state that everything is confidential. If that happens and someone discloses an item that cannot be kept in confidence, the peer support member will be seen as betraying the colleague who disclosed such information. We work diligently to make this clear up front in a manner that is not off-putting or alarming. The bottom line is that anyone who approaches peer support should be aware of limits to confidentiality.

Once a peer support team is established, it is important to let them do their work with good clinical oversight. This means team members have a consulting clinician available, should they need guidance or, most certainly, have immediate access in case of an emergency with a colleague that requires clinical direction. Peer support team members do not take notes to assure no information is leaked or subject to investigation or subpoena. They do, however, need to maintain statistics for the number of contacts they have made and the types of interventions they have completed. As budget crunches occur, one of the first things cut is typically the soft services—psychological care, peer support, and other items that are deemed a luxury. Any peer support team facing such cuts that can produce its statistics stands a good chance of keeping the program alive. Monthly and annual statistical reports must be submitted to leadership for reference.

Almost every large-scale activation that I have been called on since the bombing of the Murrah Federal Building in Oklahoma City in 1995 has included peer support. I can honestly say that having peer support makes my work much easier, and many of the activations I have done have been successful because of peer support. My peer support teams represent manpower, the ability to divide and conquer, and the ability to effectively triage personnel. It gives me the ability to focus on the bull's-eye of a situation, while team members effectively manage the outer rings.

As events occur, peer support teams often arrive before I do and have begun calming, reassuring, and caring for personnel. They have already begun to triage groups using the target method and, by the time I arrive, they typically have everything organized.

Peer support team members have instant credibility because they do the job—they walk the walk. Impacted personnel relate to them and appreciate them. My interventions are so much easier for me with peer support present. If I am working with a new group that does not know me, I have zero credibility and I have to build it from ground zero. My status as a clinician is often seen initially as a threat or something to be feared. The concern is that I will pull personnel off line or recommend they are placed on some sort of alternate status. Peer support team members reassure public safety professionals this is not the case, and that I am truly there to help impacted personnel. Facilitation of credibility means we can get to work in assisting personnel quickly and effectively.

A word of caution: As departments utilize peer support teams, it is imperative they are trained to pace themselves and each other. Peer support team members are ready and willing to give of themselves completely. When they are not paced, they will work sixteen-hour days for as many days as you ask them to. This has the potential to create a whole host of problems, including compassion fatigue, burnout, and even problems as they return to work or to their homes in attempts to resume their normal lives. Peer support is such a valuable asset, and as much as they will not want to go home and get rest or to finish an activation day early, it must be set in protocol that peer support will both activate and deactivate at the direction of someone with insight about the ways these events impact those who respond. Otherwise, team members will end up quitting the program.

One event in which I did not have peer support was in the aftermath of Hurricane Katrina. I was brought in by a federal law enforcement customer and at that time peer support was not in place at the agency. I worked really hard in a very stressful environment. It was exhausting and taxing. I did the best I could and the agents were very thankful. I had to be flown into New Orleans via helicopter due to the fact that there were no facilities for me to stay in, since I am a contractor. Every day of my work was meaningful, but would have been so much easier and more effective if I had had peer support alongside. One day, I stopped by the medical tent because I had a rash on my back. I thought it was just due to the heat and the dirt in the area. The rash turned out to be the shingles virus, due to the amount of stress I was under. The doctor in the "med shed" asked if I was stressed, at which point I looked at him defiantly and said, "No!" Of course, this was a lie. Yes, I was stressed. I remember thinking how I really needed a team to be there with me.

Chapter 10
Service Dogs and Equine Therapy

Have I told you lately that you're my best friend?
And I'll be right here beside you 'til the end
When I see you, my problems seem to slip away
You never fail to warm my nights and brighten my days

"My Best Friend" by Heidi Winzinger

I am delighted to address the importance of animals to the healing process in the final chapter of this book. I have told many patients with severe PTSD that we were going to turn over every stone to find what works in order to speed up the healing process. This means alternative methods to healing and almost always involves animals.

Pet therapy, or animal-assisted therapy, uses trained animals and handlers to achieve specific goals with patients. Studies show that contact with a pet lowers blood pressure and releases endorphins. This fact alone makes therapy dogs ideal for use in treatment settings.

Dogs

One of the best assets in my practice is my therapy dog, Tyra. The name "Tyra" means "warrior" and the fact that I gave her this name is no accident. Tyra is a beautiful, compassionate, loving black Labrador retriever mix who also happens to be a rescue. I hired a trainer to find the right dog and she looked at more than two hundred dogs before finding Tyra. We agreed I should find a dog who had the right appeal, meaning a large, beautiful, and welcoming presence. We also agreed a puppy was not the right fit. A therapy dog needs to be mellow and easy-going.

Tyra is a natural. She is amazing with my patients. She greets them and shows them down the hall to my office. She will sit and point her nose to the couch to explain to my new patients where they are supposed to sit. Tyra will tend to my patients until they are comfortable and rolling along in their session, and at that point she will curl up on her carpet. Should a patient become distressed during a session, she will jump up and comfort them immediately.

Having Tyra is an additional responsibility and I am very careful not to exploit the fact that she is a service dog. As a service dog, she is allowed to go everywhere with me, but I do not bring her to the office on days when I have multiple errands on the way home or when my work schedule will interrupt her feeding times. Tyra is, after all, a dog, and she does not need to be negatively impacted by the hectic schedule that some days bring.

Service dogs are trained to assist their owners with daily struggles that seem impossible to manage. They are extremely useful for people who are struggling with PTSD, as they are trained to assist their owner with managing their triggers. Some dogs are trained to "have the six" of their owner by maintaining a stance behind their owner to alert them to anyone approaching. Others are trained to lick their owners when they are generating a nightmare. Some dogs are trained to walk ahead of their owner around corners to "clear the corner" and let their owner know all is safe. It is absolutely incredible to watch these dogs work and the magic that happens for their owners as they return to daily functioning with the assistance of their service dog.

The requirements for service dogs are stringent. They must be well-behaved and unobtrusive in public. They must be able to perform three tasks that benefit their owner, and they must have a good temperament. Service dogs are friendly, completely nonaggressive, and reliable. Service dogs are trained to demonstrate the following cues on a consistent basis:

- Sit
- Down
- Come
- Stay
- Wait at the door
- Leave it
- Drop it
- Leash walking
- Polite human greeting
- Settle on a mat or in a crate
- House- and crate-trained
- Controlled exit and load into a vehicle
- Controlled entry and exit into a building

In addition, the dogs must be able to work with visual and auditory distractions, as well as in the presence of other dogs. Dogs are taken to a variety of locations during their training to desensitize them to various stimulating environments. Once the dog is matched with its adopter, the dog is trained to the tasks that will benefit its human companion.

Horses

Equine therapy is another amazing avenue for healing from PTSD. Studies have shown that people working with horses experience decreased blood pressure, lower stress levels, and reduced feelings of anxiety, tension, and anger. In addition, studies have shown that patients in equine therapy gain feelings of self-esteem, empowerment, patience, and trust.

Equine therapy takes advantage of the mental and physical exercise that working with a horse can provide. Interacting with a horse means dealing with and working around its moods, attitude, and personality. The primary mode for a horse is the fight-or-flight response. Based on natural survival instincts, a horse will default to fight or flight for self-preservation readily and frequently. A person with PTSD must find the ability to get grounded in order to have productive interactions with a horse. This means a patient with PTSD must learn to be in touch with their own fight-or-flight reactions and learn to manage them. What happens then is pure magic—patients with PTSD will find a rhythm and a groove with a horse. They both get grounded and calm together, and all at the same time. It is incredible to watch. Patients with PTSD learn how to manage their fight-or-flight reactions as a result of this, and the healing is well under way.

While there are many naysayers to alternative forms of therapy, my assessment of naysayers is that they have not taken the time to see such types of work in action. I encourage them to spend time with their patients and their colleagues who do this kind of work. With dogs and horses present, they will see the impact it has on their patients, including the fact that it speeds the healing process significantly.

One final word about service animals: Many fire departments are considering having service dogs attached to their stations, ready and available for their personnel. I encourage every department to consider the facts the dogs will need to have down time and off-duty time. Living at a station with the constant noise of tones dropping, rotating shifts, and the potential of being left at a station alone for long periods of time are potentially harmful to the animal. If service animals are brought on board, it quickly becomes apparent that they are assets and amazing investments. Protecting this asset the same way we protect our personnel is extremely important.

About the Author

Tania Glenn was three months from completing her Master's Degree at the University of Texas when she witnessed the dramatic and violent standoff between law enforcement and the Branch Davidian Cult in Waco, Texas. At that point, she knew her calling was to work with first responders and to focus on healing these warriors from the horrors of post-traumatic stress disorder.

Tania spent the first ten years of her career working in a Level Two Trauma Emergency Department on weekend nights as she built her private practice during the week. In 2002, Tania transitioned to her private practice on a full-time basis and has dedicated her entire career to working with first responders and military members.

Tania assisted with the aftermath of the Oklahoma City Murrah Federal Building bombing, the 9/11 attacks on the World Trade Center, Hurricane Katrina, the Dallas Police shootings, and numerous other incidents. Tania is referred to as the "warrior healer" by her colleagues, and she is passionate about her work.

Tania resides in Central Texas. Her loves include her family, her pets, and fitness.

Progressive Rising Phoenix Press is an independent publisher. We offer wholesale discounts and multiple binding options with no minimum purchases for schools, libraries, book clubs, and retail vendors. We also offer rewards for libraries, schools, independent book stores, and book clubs. Please visit our website and wholesale discount page at:

www.ProgressiveRisingPhoenix.com

Progressive Rising Phoenix Press is adding new titles from our award-winning authors on a regular basis and has books in the following genres: children's chapter books and picture books, middle grade, young adult, action adventure, mystery and suspense, contemporary fiction, romance, historical fiction, fantasy, science fiction, and non-fiction covering a variety of topics from military to inspirational to biographical. Visit our website to see our updated catalogue of titles.

CPSIA information can be obtained
at www.ICGtesting.com
Printed in the USA
LVHW052342160919
631220LV00006BA/1188/P